MACMILLAN LITERATURE COLLECTIONS

Horror Stories

edited by Ceri Jones

HARROW COLLEGE
Learning Centre
020 8909 6520 (HH)
020 8909 6248 (HW)

MACMILLAN

Macmillan Education
4 Crinan Street
London N1 9XW
A division of Macmillan Publishers Limited
Companies and representatives throughout the world

ISBN 978–0–2307–1693–3

All additional material written by Ceri Jones

First published 2009
Text © Macmillan Publishers Limited 2009
Design and illustration © Macmillan Publishers Limited 2009

The authors and publishers are grateful for permission to reprint the following
copyright material:

Arkham House Publishers Inc. for the story 'Smoke Ghost' by Fritz Leiber,
originally published in *Unknown Worlds*, copyright © 1941. Reproduced
with permission of Arkham House Publishers Inc.;

David Higham Associates for the story 'A Spot of Gothic' by Jane Gardam,
originally published in *The Sidmouth Letters* published by Little Brown.
Reproduced with permission of David Higham Associated Limited.

These materials may contain links for third party websites. We have no
control over, and are not responsible for, the contents of such third party
websites. Please use care when accessing them.

Cover by Rex Features/Everett Collection

Printed and bound in Thailand

2017   2016   2015
11   10   9   8   7

Contents

Macmillan Literature Collections

Welcome to the *Macmillan Literature Collections* – a series of advanced-level readers containing original, unsimplified short stories written by famous classic and modern writers. We hope that these stories will help to ease students' transition from graded readers to reading authentic novels.

Each collection in the series includes:

Introduction

– an introduction to the short story
– tips for reading authentic texts in English
– an introduction to the genre
– a carefully-chosen selection of classic and modern short stories.

The stories

Each story is presented in three parts: the introduction and pre-reading support material; the story; and post-reading activities. Each part includes the following sections:

– *About the author* – in-depth information about the author and their work
– *About the story* – information about the story, including background information about setting and cultural references
– *Summary* – a brief summary of the story that does not give away the ending.

Pre-reading exercises

– *Key vocabulary* – a chance to look at some of the more difficult vocabulary related to the main themes and style of the story before reading the story
– *Main themes* – a brief discussion of the main themes, with questions to keep in mind as you read.

The story

You will find numbered footnotes in the stories. These explain cultural and historical references, and key words that you will need to understand the text. Many of these footnotes give definitions of words which are very formal, old-fashioned or rarely used in modern English. You will find more common, useful words and phrases from the stories in the *Glossary* at the end of the book. Words included in the *Glossary* will appear in **bold**.

Post-reading exercises

- *Understanding the story* – comprehension questions that will help you make sure you've understood the story
- *Language study* – a section that presents and practises key linguistic and structural features of authentic literary texts (you will find an index of the areas covered at the end of the book)
- *Literary analysis* – discussion questions that guide you to an in-depth appreciation of the story, its structure, its characters and its style.

In addition, at the end of each book there are:
- suggested *Essay questions*
- a comprehensive *Glossary* highlighting useful vocabulary from each story
- an **index** for the *Language study* section.

How to use these books

You can use these books in whatever way you want. You may want to start from the beginning and work your way through. You may want to pick and choose. The *Contents* page gives a very brief, one-line introduction to each story to help you decide where to start. You may want to learn about the author and the story before you read each one, or you may prefer to read the story first and then find out more about it afterwards. Remember that the stories and exercises can be challenging, so you may want to spend quite a long time studying each one. The most important thing is to enjoy the collection – to enjoy reading, to enjoy the stories and to enjoy the language that has been used to create them.

—

Answer keys

In many cases you can check your answers in the story by using the page references given. However, an Answer key for all the exercises will be available on the student's section of the Macmillan Readers website at www.macmillanenglish.com/readers

Introduction

What is a short story?

A short story is shorter than a novel, but longer than a poem. It is usually between 1,000 and 20,000 words long. It tells a story which can usually be read quite quickly. It often concentrates on one, central event; it has a limited number of characters, and takes place within a short space of time.

History of the short story

Stories and storytelling have existed for as long as people have had language. People love, and need, stories. They help us explain and understand the world. Before people could read or write, storytellers travelled from village to village, telling stories.

The first written stories developed from this storytelling tradition. Two of the best-known examples of early, written stories in Europe appeared in the 14th century. Chaucer's *Canterbury Tales* and Bocaccio's *Decameron* are both based on the same idea – a group of people who are travelling or living together for a short time, agree to tell each other stories.

The first modern short stories appeared at the beginning of the 19th century. Early examples of short-story collections include the *Fairy Tales* (1824–26) of the Brothers Grimm, and Edgar Allan Poe's *Tales of the Grotesque and Arabesque* (1840). In the late 19th century, printed magazines and journals became very popular and more and more short stories were published. By the 20th century most well-known magazines included short stories in every issue and the publishers paid a lot of money for them. In 1952 Ernest Hemingway's short story, *The Old Man and the Sea*, helped sell more than five million copies of the magazine *Life* in just two days.

The short story today

Today, short stories are often published in collections called anthologies. They are usually grouped according to a particular category – by theme, topic, national origin, time, or author. Some newspapers and magazines continue to print individual stories. Many short stories are first published on the Internet, with authors posting them on special-interest websites and in online magazines.

Reading authentic literary texts in English

Reading authentic literary texts can be difficult. They may contain grammatical structures you have not studied, or expressions and sayings you are not familiar with. Unlike graded readers, they have not been written for language students. The words have been chosen to create a particular effect, not because they are easy or difficult. But you do not need to understand every word to understand and enjoy the story.

When you are reading in your own language you will often read so quickly that you skip over words, and read for the general effect, rather than the details. Try to do the same when you are reading in English. Remember that looking up every word you don't know slows you down and stops you enjoying the story.

When you're reading authentic short stories, remember:
- It should be a pleasure!
- You should read at your own pace.
- Let the story carry you along – don't worry about looking up every word you don't understand.
- Don't worry about looking up difficult words unless they stop you from understanding the story.
- Try not to use the *Glossary* or a dictionary when you're reading.

You might want to make a note of words to look up later, especially key words that you see several times (see *Using a dictionary* on page 9 for more tips on looking up and recording new words). But remember, you can always go back again when you have finished the story. That is the beauty of reading short stories – they are short! You can finish one quite quickly, especially if you do not worry about understanding every single word; then you can start again at the beginning and take your time to re-read difficult passages and look up key words.

Preparing yourself for a story

It is always a good idea to prepare yourself, mentally, before starting a story.
- Look at the title. What does it tell you about the story? What do you expect the story to be about?
- If there is a summary, read it. This will help you follow the story.

- Quickly read the first few paragraphs and answer these questions:
  Where is it set?
  When is it set?
  Who is the main character?
- As you read, concentrate on following the gist (the general idea) of the story. You can go back and look at the details later. You can use the questions at the end of the story (see *Understanding the story*) to help you understand what is happening.

Tips for dealing with difficult passages

Some stories include particularly difficult passages. They are usually descriptive and give background information, or set the scene. They are generally difficult to follow because they are full of detail. Try to read these passages quickly, understanding what you can, and then continue with the story. Make a note of the passage and come back to it later, when you have finished the whole story.

If, at any time, you are finding it difficult to follow the story, go back to this difficult passage. It may hold the answers to your questions.

Read through the passage again carefully and underline all the unknown words. Try to understand as much as you can from the immediate context and what you now know about the story. Then, look up any remaining words in the *Glossary* at the back of the book, or in your dictionary.

Tips for dealing with difficult words

- Decide if the word (or phrase) is important to the overall message. Read the whole paragraph. Do you understand the general meaning? Yes? Then the word isn't important. Don't worry about it. *Keep reading!*
- If you decide the word is important, see if you can work out its meaning from the context. Is it a verb, a noun or an adjective? Is it positive or negative? How would you translate it into in your own language? Underline the word or make a note of it and the page number, but *keep reading*. If it really is important, you'll see it again.
- If you keep seeing the same word in the story, and you still can't understand it, look in your monolingual dictionary!

Using a dictionary

Looking up words

Before you look up the word, look at it again in its context. Decide what part of speech it is. Try to guess its meaning from the context. Now look it up in your dictionary. There may be more than one definition given. Decide which one is the most appropriate. If the word is something very specific, eg the name of a flower or tree, you can use a bilingual dictionary to give you the exact translation.

Let's look at how this works in practice. Look at this short extract and follow the instructions below.

> ...there is a little valley or rather **lap** of land among high hills, which is one of the quietest places in the whole world. A small **brook** glides through it, with just murmur enough to **lull** one to repose*
>
> *literary: sleep or rest*
> *The Legend of Sleepy Hollow* by Washington Irvine

1 Look at the words in bold and decide what part of speech they are – noun, verb, adjective, etc.
2 Try to guess what they might mean.
3 Look at the extracts below from the *Macmillan English Dictionary for Advanced Learners*. Choose the most appropriate definition.

Words with more than one entry Sometimes the same word belongs to more than one word class: for example, *brook* can be both a noun and a verb. Each word class is shown as a separate entry. The small number at the end of the head-word tells you that a word has more than one entry. **Idioms and fixed expressions** Some words are often used in idioms and fixed expressions. These are shown at the end of the entry, following the small box that says PHRASE. **Words with more than one meaning** Many words have more than one meaning, and each different meaning is shown by a number.	**brook¹** noun a small river **brook²** verb **not brook** – to definitely not allow or accept something. **lap¹** noun **1** the top half of your legs above your knees when you sit down. **2** one complete turn around a course in a race PHRASE in the lap of luxury in very comfortable and expensive conditions **lap²** verb **1** if an animal laps water, it drinks it gently with its tongue **lull¹** noun a quiet period during a very active or violent situation **lull²** verb **1** to make someone feel relaxed and confident so that they are not prepared for something unpleasant to happen to lull someone into a false sense of security **2** to make someone relaxed enough to go to sleep

Dictionary extracts adapted from the Macmillan English Dictionary © Macmillan Publishers Limited 2002.

Keeping a record

When you have looked in your dictionary, decide if the word is interesting or useful to you. If it is, make a note of it, and write down its definition. Make a note of the sentence where you found it in the story, then write one or two more examples of your own. Only do this for those words you think you will need to use in the future.

Here is an example of how you might record the word *lull*.

'with just murmur enough to lull one to repose'
Lull – to make you feel relaxed enough to go to sleep
e.g. The quiet sound of the waves lulled me to sleep
The mother sang to her baby to lull it to sleep

Literary analysis

The *Literary analysis* section is written to encourage you to consider the stories in more depth. This will help you to appreciate them better and develop your analytical skills. This section is particularly useful for those students who are studying, or intending to study, literature in the medium of English. Each section includes literary terms with which you may or may not be familiar.

Macmillan Readers student's website

For more help with understanding these literary terms, and to find Answer keys to all the exercises and activities, visit the student's section of the Macmillan Readers' website at <u>www.macmillanenglish.com/readers</u>. There you will also find a wealth of resources to help your language learning in English; from listening exercises to articles on acedemic and creative writing.

The genre of Horror

What is Horror?

A horror story is a story that is intended to frighten people. Horror stories can describe very real events, such as being attacked by a stranger in your home, or being trapped underground or in a fire. They also often talk about the supernatural world and things such as ghosts, monsters, or vampires. There is almost always an element of evil – a clever serial killer or an angry ghost, although sometimes the cause of the horror is in the main character's imagination.

Why do we like horror stories?

People enjoy horror stories because they enjoy being frightened. Reading them is exciting; it releases adrenalin. Horror stories are a safe way of facing our fears. That is why horror has always played an important part in storytelling, from the myths and legends of early civilisations to modern horror movies.

Modern horror fiction in English

The first modern horror stories in English were those told in the gothic[1] novels of the 18th and early 19th century. They spoke of ghosts that haunted[2] ruined castles in quiet and lonely places. Mary Shelley's *Frankenstein*, published in 1818, is one of the best-known horror stories of all time. Bram Stoker's *Dracula*, published in 1897, was another classic that influenced generations of horror writers.

Short stories and horror

Horror fits perfectly into the short-story format because it lets the author concentrate on unusual events or mysteries. The atmosphere and setting are as important as the plot, and the stories quickly build to a dramatic climax.

The first American horror story to be published was Washington Irving's *The Legend of Sleepy Hollow* (1820), the tale of a small village, lost in time and haunted by a headless horseman.

1   with frightening and mysterious subjects
2   visited (by the spirit of a dead person)

Edgar Allan Poe, H.P. Lovecraft, and M.R. James are all considered to be great short horror story writers. Between them they wrote hundreds of horror stories. All three writers avoided using physical violence. Many modern day short horror stories tend to be more explicit and contain more graphic violence.

Today's 'master of horror' is, undoubtedly, Stephen King, the creator of horror stories such as *The Shining, Carrie* and *Children of the Corn*. He has written more than 100 short stories, most of them horror stories.

Other forms

Horror stories are not only found in literature, they are also very popular in the cinema. Classic horror stories are very popular subjects for film-makers. Many films have been based on horror novels and short stories, including *Frankenstein, Dracula, Interview with a Vampire*, and *Sleepy Hollow* – there are many more.

There are also comic films which take a classic horror story, theme or character and turn it into comedy, for example, *Frankenstein Junior* or the cult movie, *The Rocky Horror Show*.

There are many horror television series, such as *The X-files* and *Buffy the Vampire Slayer*; video games, such as *Resident Evil* and *Doom*, also contain elements of horror in their story lines and gameplay.

The Terror of Blue John Gap

by Sir Arthur Conan Doyle

About the author

Sir Arthur Conan Doyle is best known as the creator of the great fictional detective, Sherlock Holmes. As well as the Sherlock Holmes stories, he also wrote science fiction and horror stories, historical novels, and political pamphlets[1]. During his lifetime, he achieved a great deal, and was greatly admired in the world of medicine as well as in the arts. Throughout his life, he was interested in explaining the unexplainable, and finding answers to all kinds of problems: real life criminal cases, political issues, and even the question of whether there is life after death.

Arthur Doyle (he added 'Conan' later in life) was born in Edinburgh, Scotland, on 22 May, 1859 to an English father and an Irish mother. After finishing school, he studied medicine. In his spare time, he began to write stories, which were published in various magazines.

After serving for a short time as a ship's doctor, he started working in a private medical practice, first in Southsea and then later in London. But business was slow, he had very few patients and he had to write stories to make money.

In 1887, his first important work was published, A *Study in Scarlet*. This was his first Sherlock Holmes novel. The second Sherlock Holmes novel, *The Sign of the Four* (1890), was followed by the first Sherlock Holmes short story, A *Scandal in Bohemia* (1891). Other short stories soon followed, published as regular monthly features in the *Strand Magazine*.

During the same period, Conan Doyle also wrote a series of successful historical novels. He soon realised that he could make more money writing than working as a doctor, and he decided to become a full-time writer.

In 1900, the author went to South Africa to work as a field doctor during the Boer War. He wrote an account of the war, *War in South Africa: Its Cause and Conduct*, defending the role of the British army

---

1 short books about political or social problems

in South Africa. In the same year, he was given a knighthood[2] for his services to his country, and became 'Sir' Arthur Conan Doyle.

In the 1900s, Sir Arthur Conan Doyle became interested in politics. He stood for parliament twice, but was not elected. He supported the movement for women's rights and wrote a book, *The Crime of the Congo*, describing the horrors in that country. He also investigated two crimes that had already been solved by the police. In both investigations, Conan Doyle discovered that the police had been wrong and, as a result, two innocent men were freed from prison.

Sir Arthur Conan Doyle's wife died in 1906, and shortly afterwards so did his sons, Kingsley and Innes. Some time after the First World War, the author sank into a depression. He was spending less time writing, and more time studying spiritualism and carrying out scientific research into the existence of life after death. He died of a heart attack in 1930 at the age of seventy-one.

About the story

The story *The Terror of Blue John Gap* was first published in 1912, and was later included in the collection, *Tales of Terror and Mystery*, along with another 11 stories by Sir Arthur Conan Doyle. The collection was published in 1923.

Background information

The story is set in the English county of Derbyshire, in the Peak District, near the village of Castleton. The main action takes place in the old, disused Blue John mines in the area.

Blue John Stone

Blue John Stone is a rare, semi-precious mineral. The name Blue John comes from the French *Bleu Jaune* meaning 'blue yellow'. It was discovered by miners who were looking for lead.

There are four show-caves near Castleton, in the Peak District, which are open to visitors. Treak Cliff Cavern still mines about 500 kg of Blue John Stone each year.

---

2 an honour given by the British King or Queen which allows a man to use the title 'Sir' before his name

Tuberculosis

Tuberculosis was a very common disease at the time the story is set (1906). It was responsible for one in four deaths in England in 1815, and at the time of the story, it was still a major health problem. Its symptoms include high fever and tiredness. It was believed that the fever could cause hallucinations[3].

The main character, Dr James Hardcastle, is suffering from tuberculosis. Doctors thought that fresh air and exercise could help fight the disease. Many middle- and upper-class patients were sent to the mountains as part of their treatment.

3 something that you think you can see or hear that is not really there

Summary

It may help you to know something about what happens in the story before you read it. Don't worry, this summary does not tell you how the story ends!

The story is written as a series of diary entries, which the narrator, Dr James Hardcastle, leaves to be found after his death. The person who introduces the story describes Hardcastle as a rational and scientific man. The tale itself is told in Hardcastle's own words.

Dr Hardcastle has been sent to the country to recover from tuberculosis. He is staying on a farm, near the town of Castleton, in the Peak District. He spends his time walking in the hills, and he becomes interested in the old disused mines and caves under the hills.

A local man, named Armitage, tells Dr Hardcastle about the legend of the terror of Blue John Gap. Local people say there is a monster that lives in the underground caves and comes out at night to steal sheep. Armitage says he has heard the monster. Dr Hardcastle is surprised by how **superstitious** the locals are, until he hears the strange noise, too. He decides to explore the cave when he is feeling stronger.

Dr Hardcastle starts to explore the entrance (or 'mouth') of the cave, and wonders if it is possible that some kind of strange creature lives in the underground caves. When he is in the caves, his candle goes out and he is left in the dark.

He hears strange noises and feels the presence of the monster. He immediately runs out of the caves, frightened by his experience, and then he decides to tell someone about what happened. He goes to visit a local doctor. The doctor refers him to a specialist, but Dr Hardcastle chooses not to talk to him.

At the same time, sheep go missing on the hills near Blue John Gap. When Armitage, the local who first told Dr Hardcastle about the monster, also goes missing, Dr Hardcastle decides to tell the police about his experience in the cave. But the police laugh at him, so Dr Hardcastle decides to face the monster on his own. He buys a lantern (a lamp/light) and a rifle (a kind of gun), and leaves a note in his bedroom, telling his hosts to look for him in Blue John Gap if he goes missing.

Pre-reading exercises

Key vocabulary

This section will help to familiarise you with some of the more specific vocabulary used in the story. You may want to use it to help you before you start reading, or as a revision exercise after you've finished the story.

The story has many descriptive passages. These passages contain very specific words to describe movements and sounds and to give detailed descriptions of the underground passage.

Verbs describing movement

1 Read the definitions below, and picture the movements in your mind. Most of the verbs describe the movements of the main character, Dr Hardcastle, when he is in the underground cave. Which ones do you think describe the movement of the mysterious creature he meets there?

crouch to move your body close to the ground by bending your knees
flounder to move with great difficulty and be in danger of falling
grope to try to find something by feeling with your hands
lurch to move suddenly in an uncontrolled manner
rear up when a four-legged animal stands up on its two back legs
stagger to walk in an uncontrolled way as if you are going to fall over
stoop to walk or stand with your head and shoulders bent forward

When you have finished the story, look back at this page and check your answers.

Nouns used to refer to the underground caves and passages

2 Look at the nouns and their definitions, listed below. Replace the phrases in bold with nouns from the list.

burrow a tunnel or hole in the ground built by an animal in order to live in it
chamber a large room or an enclosed space
chasm a very deep crack in rock or ice
labyrinth a place where there are a lot of paths and passages and you can easily get lost
shaft a long narrow passage, for example, one that leads from the surface of the ground down to a mine

1 The mountaineers traversed until they reached a **steep drop**.
2 Rabbits had created **holes** all over the hillside.
3 The miners used a lift to go down the **vertical passageway**.
4 Suddenly the archeologists found themselves in a large **room**.
5 The old market was a **confusing series of small passageways**.

Describing the entrance to Blue John Gap

3 Look at this description of the entrance to Blue John Gap. Complete the description with the phrases in the box below.

> marked, covered   wet earth   small, dry branches   coat of wool
> confused   large rocks   thorns   small bits of wool

The entrance to Blue John Gap is described in detail. There are plants around it, **briars**, a bush with (1) .... (sharp points), and **brushwood**, (2) .... that have fallen from nearby trees. **Tufts of wool** are caught in the thorns of the briars – these are (3) .... that have been pulled from a sheep's **fleece** (the sheep's (4) ....) as it went past. The tufts of wool are **smeared** (5) (..............................) with blood. Inside the passage there are **boulders** (6) (..............................), and **mud** (7) (..............................) which can easily show footprints. It is an easy place to **lose your bearings**, to become (8) .... about where you are and lose your way.

Describing sounds

4 The following sounds all add to the atmosphere of the story. Most are heard either in the underground passages, or coming from the passages. Match the sounds described in the list below, to the words in the box.

> a lion   a stream   footsteps   a car horn   thunder   a falling rock   a dog

> **boom** a deep sound that continues for some time
> **crash** a loud noise like the sound of two hard things hitting each other
> **gurgle** the low sound that water makes when it is poured from a bottle
> **hoot** a short, loud sound, like an owl's call
> **muffled** a sound which is quiet and not easy to hear
> **roar** a deep, loud sound, often made in anger
> **whine** a low, complaining sound, like that of an animal in pain

Main themes

Before you read the story, you may want to think about some of its main themes. The questions will help you think about the story as you're reading it for the first time. There is more discussion of the main themes in in the *Literary analysis* section after the story.

Mythical monsters

The main subject matter of the story is a legendary creature which locals believe lives in the caves under the local hills. No-one has seen the creature, but they claim that it kills sheep on the surrounding hillsides.

Folk stories from all over the world, both past and present, are full of creatures like this – stories about mythical beasts that few people have seen, but many have tried to prove their existence, such as the Yeti or the Loch Ness Monster. Greek mythology speaks of a terrifying monster, the Minotaur, half-man, half-bull, who lives in an underground labyrinth.

5 As you read the story, ask yourself:

a) Does the monster really exist?
b) Does the story remind you of any other similar stories you have read, heard or seen?

Superstition versus science

One of the main themes of the story is the argument between superstitious fears and scientific explanations. This is a theme that appears in a lot of Conan Doyle's fiction, especially in the Sherlock Holmes stories. The main character in this story, Dr Hardcastle, tries to bring together superstition and science. He starts from a position of total scepticism[4], but slowly he comes to believe that there must be some truth behind the legend and he tries to find a rational, scientific explanation.

6 As you read the story, ask yourself:

a) Why does Dr Hardcastle feel it is so important to find out the truth about the beast?
b) Why does he think he is the right person to do it?
c) Are you convinced by Dr Hardcastle's scientific explanation?

4 not believing

Madness and hallucinations

Dr Hardcastle is suffering from tuberculosis – a disease which can make people hallucinate. Some of the characters in the story, including Dr Hardcastle himself, suggest that he may be imagining things (seeing or hearing things that are not really there) or going mad.

7 As you read the story, ask yourself:

a) Can we believe Dr Hardcastle? Is he telling us what really happened?

b) Is it simply his imagination?

The Terror of Blue John Gap

by Sir Arthur Conan Doyle

The following narrative was found among the papers of Dr. James Hardcastle, who died of phthisis[5] on February 4th, 1908, at 36, Upper Coventry Flats, South Kensington. Those who knew him best, while refusing to express an opinion upon[6] this particular statement, are unanimous in asserting that he was a man of a sober and scientific turn of mind, absolutely devoid of imagination, and most unlikely to invent any abnormal series of events. The paper was contained in an envelope, which was docketed,[7] 'A Short Account of the Circumstances which occurred near Miss Allerton's Farm in North-West Derbyshire in the Spring of Last Year.' The envelope was sealed, and on the other side was written in pencil –

DEAR SEATON, –

'It may interest, and perhaps pain you, to know that the incredulity with which you met my story has prevented me from ever opening my mouth upon the subject again. I leave this record after my death, and perhaps strangers may be found to have more confidence in me than my friend.'

Inquiry has failed to elicit who this Seaton may have been. I may add that the visit of the deceased to Allerton's Farm, and the general nature of the alarm there, apart from his particular explanation, have been absolutely established. With this foreword I append his account exactly as he left it. It is in the form of a diary, some entries in which have been expanded, while a few have been erased.

April 17. Already I feel the benefit of this wonderful upland air.

5   the Greek word for tuberculosis
6   *literary:* on
7   *old-fashioned:* had the title

The farm of the Allertons lies fourteen hundred and twenty feet above sea-level, so it may well be a bracing climate. Beyond the usual morning cough I have very little discomfort, and, what with the fresh milk and the home-grown mutton, I have every chance of putting on weight. I think Saunderson will be pleased.

The two Miss Allertons are charmingly quaint and kind, two dear little hard-working old maids, who are ready to lavish all the heart which might have gone out to husband and to children upon an invalid stranger. Truly, the old maid[8] is a most useful person, one of the reserve forces of the community. They talk of the superfluous woman, but what would the poor superfluous man do without her kindly presence? By the way, in their simplicity they very quickly let out the reason why Saunderson recommended their farm. The Professor **rose from the ranks** himself, and I believe that in his youth he was not above scaring crows in these very fields.

It is a most lonely spot, and the walks are picturesque in the extreme. The farm consists of grazing land lying at the bottom of an irregular valley. On each side are the fantastic limestone hills, formed of rock so soft that you can break it away with your hands. All this country is hollow. Could you strike it with some gigantic hammer it would boom like a drum, or possibly cave in altogether and expose some huge subterranean sea. A great sea there must surely be, for on all sides the streams run into the mountain itself, never to reappear. There are gaps everywhere amid the rocks, and when you pass through them you find yourself in great caverns, which wind down into the bowels of the earth. I have a small bicycle lamp, and it is a perpetual joy to me to carry it into these weird solitudes[9], and to see the wonderful silver and black effect when I throw its light upon the stalactites which drape the lofty[10] roofs. Shut off the lamp, and you are in the blackest darkness. Turn it on, and it is a scene from the Arabian Nights.[11]

8 *mainly old-fashioned:* a woman who has not married or had children
9 *old-fashioned:* lonely places
10 *mainly literary:* very tall
11 a collection of Middle Eastern folk tales

But there is one of these strange openings in the earth which has a special interest, for it is the handiwork, not of nature, but of man. I had never heard of Blue John when I came to these parts. It is the name given to a peculiar mineral of a beautiful purple shade, which is only found at one or two places in the world. It is so rare that an ordinary vase of Blue John would be valued at a great price. The Romans, with that extraordinary instinct of theirs, discovered that it was to be found in this valley, and sank a horizontal shaft deep into the mountain side. The opening of their mine has been called Blue John Gap, a clean-cut arch in the rock, the mouth all overgrown with bushes. It is a goodly[12] passage which the Roman miners have cut, and it intersects some of the great water-worn caves, so that if you enter Blue John Gap you would do well to mark your steps and to have a good store of candles, or you may never **make your way** back to the daylight again. I have not yet gone deeply into it, but this very day I stood at the mouth of the arched tunnel, and **peering** down into the black recesses beyond, I **vowed** that when my health returned I would devote some holiday to exploring those mysterious depths and finding out for myself how far the Romans had penetrated into the Derbyshire hills.

Strange how superstitious these countrymen are! I should have thought better of young Armitage, for he is a man of some education and character, and a very fine fellow[13] for his station[14] in life. I was standing at the Blue John Gap when he came across the field to me.

'Well, doctor,' said he, 'you're not afraid, anyhow.'

'Afraid!' I answered. 'Afraid of what?'

'Of it,' said he, with a jerk of his thumb towards the black vault, 'of the Terror that lives in the Blue John Cave.'

How absurdly easy it is for a legend to arise in a lonely countryside![15] I examined[16] him as to the reasons for his weird belief. It seems that from time to time sheep have been missing

12 *old-fashioned:* well made
13 *old-fashioned:* a good man
14 *old-fashioned:* position in society
15 countryside is not countable in modern usage
16 *mainly legal:* questioned

from the fields, carried bodily away, according to Armitage. That they could have wandered away of their own accord and disappeared among the mountains was an explanation to which he would not listen. On one occasion a pool of blood had been found, and some tufts of wool. That also, I pointed out, could be explained in a perfectly natural way. Further, the nights upon which[17] sheep disappeared were invariably very dark, cloudy nights with no moon. This I met with the obvious retort that those were the nights which a **commonplace** sheep-stealer would naturally choose for his work. On one occasion a gap had been made in a wall, and some of the stones scattered for a considerable distance. Human agency[18] again, in my opinion. Finally, Armitage **clinched all his arguments** by telling me that he had actually heard the Creature – indeed, that anyone could hear it who remained long enough at the Gap. It was a distant roaring of an immense volume. I could not but smile at this, knowing, as I do, the strange reverberations which come out of an underground water system running amid the chasms of a limestone formation. My incredulity annoyed Armitage so that he turned and left me with some abruptness.

And now comes the queer point about the whole business. I was still standing near the mouth of the cave turning over in my mind the various statements of Armitage, and reflecting how readily they could be **explained away**, when suddenly, from the depth of the tunnel beside me, there issued[19] a most extraordinary sound. How shall I describe it? First of all, it seemed to be a great distance away, far down in the bowels of the earth. Secondly, in spite of this suggestion of distance, it was very loud. Lastly, it was not a boom, nor a crash, such as one[20] would associate with falling water or tumbling rock, but it was a high whine, tremulous and vibrating, almost like the whinnying of a horse. It was certainly a most remarkable experience, and

17 *old-fashioned:* when
18 *formal:* a person was responsible for the action
19 *literary:* come out
20 *formal:* the pronoun *one* is used here instead of *you* to talk about something which is true for people in general, including yourself

one which for a moment, I must admit, gave a new significance to Armitage's words. I waited by the Blue John Gap for half an hour or more, but there was no return of the sound, so at last I wandered back to the farmhouse, rather mystified by what had occurred. Decidedly I shall explore that cavern when my strength is restored. Of course, Armitage's explanation is too absurd for discussion, and yet that sound was certainly very strange. It still rings in my ears as I write.

April 20. In the last three days I have made several expeditions to the Blue John Gap, and have even penetrated some short distance, but my bicycle lantern is so small and weak that I dare not trust myself very far. I shall do the thing more systematically. I have heard no sound at all, and could almost believe that I had been the victim of some hallucination suggested, perhaps, by Armitage's conversation. Of course, the whole idea is absurd, and yet I must confess that those bushes at the entrance of the cave do present an appearance as if some heavy creature had forced its way through them. I begin to be keenly interested. I have said nothing to the Miss Allertons, for they are quite superstitious enough already, but I have bought some candles, and mean to investigate for myself.

I observed this morning that among the numerous tufts of sheep's wool which lay among the bushes near the cavern there was one which was smeared with blood. Of course, my reason tells me that if sheep wander into such rocky places they are likely to injure themselves, and yet somehow that splash of crimson gave me a sudden shock, and for a moment I found myself **shrinking back** in horror from the old Roman arch. A fetid[21] breath seemed to ooze from the black depths into which I peered. Could it indeed be possible that some nameless thing, some dreadful presence, was **lurking** down yonder[22]? I should[23] have been incapable of such feelings in the days of my strength,

---

21 *formal*: bad smelling
22 *old-fashioned*: below
23 old-fashioned use of the auxiliary *should*; in modern usage we use *would*

but one grows more nervous and fanciful when one's health is shaken.

For the moment I weakened in my resolution, and was ready to leave the secret of the old mine, if one exists, for ever unsolved. But tonight my interest has returned and my nerves grown more steady. Tomorrow I trust that I shall have gone more deeply into this matter.

April 22. Let me try and **set down** as accurately as I can my extraordinary experience of yesterday. I started in the afternoon, and made my way to the Blue John Gap. I confess that my misgivings returned as I gazed into its depths, and I wished that I had brought a companion to share my exploration. Finally, with a return of resolution, I lit my candle, pushed my way through the briars, and descended into the rocky shaft.

It went down at an acute angle for some fifty feet, the floor being covered with broken stone. Thence[24] there extended a long, straight passage cut in the solid rock. I am no geologist, but the lining of this corridor was certainly of some harder material than limestone, for there were points where I could actually see the tool-marks which the old miners had left in their excavation, as fresh as if they had been done yesterday. Down this strange, old-world corridor I stumbled, my feeble flame throwing a dim circle of light around me, which made the shadows beyond the more threatening and obscure. Finally, I came to a spot where the Roman tunnel opened into a water-worn cavern – a huge hall, hung with long white icicles of lime deposit. From this central chamber I could dimly perceive that a number of passages worn by the subterranean streams wound away into the depths of the earth. I was standing there wondering whether I had better return, or whether I dare venture farther into this dangerous labyrinth, when my eyes fell upon something at my feet which strongly arrested[25] my attention.

The greater part of the floor of the cavern was covered

24 *old-fashioned:* from there
25 *formal:* caught

with boulders of rock or with hard incrustations of lime, but at this particular point there had been a drip from the distant roof, which had left a patch of soft mud. In the very centre of this there was a huge mark – an ill-defined blotch, deep, broad and irregular, as if a great boulder had fallen upon it. No loose stone lay near, however, nor was there anything to account for the impression. It was far too large to be caused by any possible animal, and besides, there was only the one, and the patch of mud was of such a size that no reasonable stride could have covered it. As I rose from the examination of that singular[26] mark and then looked round into the black shadows which hemmed me in, I must confess that I felt for a moment a most unpleasant sinking of my heart, and that, do what I could, the candle trembled in my outstretched hand.

I soon recovered my nerve, however, when I reflected how absurd it was to associate so huge and shapeless a mark with the track of any known animal. Even an elephant could not have produced it. I determined[27], therefore, that I would not be scared by vague and senseless fears from carrying out my exploration. Before proceeding, I took good note of a curious rock formation in the wall by which I could recognize the entrance of the Roman tunnel. The precaution was very necessary, for the great cave, so far as I could see it, was intersected by passages. Having made sure of my position, and reassured myself by examining my spare candles and my matches, I advanced slowly over the rocky and uneven surface of the cavern.

And now I come to the point where I met with such sudden and desperate disaster. A stream, some twenty feet broad, ran across my path, and I walked for some little distance along the bank to find a spot where I could cross dry-shod[28]. Finally, I came to a place where a single flat boulder lay near the centre, which I could reach in a stride. As it chanced[29], however, the rock had been cut away and made top-heavy by the rush of the stream,

26 *mainly literary:* strange or unusual
27 *formal:* decided
28 *old-fashioned:* without getting my feet wet
29 *old-fashioned:* happened

so that it tilted over as I landed on it and shot me into the ice-cold water. My candle went out, and I found myself floundering about in **utter** and absolute darkness.

I staggered to my feet again, more amused than alarmed by my adventure. The candle had fallen from my hand, and was lost in the stream, but I had two others in my pocket, so that it was of no importance. I got one of them ready, and drew out my box of matches to light it. Only then did I realize my position. The box had been **soaked** in my fall into the river. It was impossible to strike the matches.

A cold hand seemed to close round my heart as I realized my position. The darkness was opaque and horrible. It was so utter, one put one's hand up to one's face as if to press off something solid. I stood still, and by an effort I steadied myself. I tried to reconstruct in my mind a map of the floor of the cavern as I had last seen it. Alas![30] the bearings which had impressed themselves upon my mind were high on the wall, and not to be found by touch. Still, I remembered in a general way how the sides were situated, and I hoped that by groping my way along them I should at last come to the opening of the Roman tunnel. Moving very slowly, and continually striking against the rocks, I set out on this desperate quest.

But I very soon realized how impossible it was. In that black, velvety darkness one lost all one's bearings in an instant. Before I had made a dozen paces, I was utterly bewildered as to my whereabouts. The rippling of the stream, which was the one sound audible, showed me where it lay, but the moment that I left its bank I was utterly lost. The idea of finding my way back in absolute darkness through that limestone labyrinth was clearly an impossible one.

I sat down upon a boulder and reflected upon my unfortunate plight. I had not told anyone that I proposed to come to the Blue John mine, and it was unlikely that a search party would come after me. Therefore I must trust to my own resources to get clear of the danger. There was only one hope, and that was

30 *old-fashioned*: unfortunately

that the matches might dry. When I fell into the river, only half of me had got thoroughly wet. My left shoulder had remained above the water. I took the box of matches, therefore, and put it into my left armpit. The moist air of the cavern might possibly be counteracted by the heat of my body, but even so, I knew that I could not hope to get a light for many hours. Meanwhile there was nothing for it but to wait.

By good luck I had slipped several biscuits into my pocket before I left the farm-house. These I now devoured, and washed them down with a draught[31] from that wretched stream which had been the cause of all my misfortunes. Then I felt about for a comfortable seat among the rocks, and, having discovered a place where I could get a support for my back, I stretched out my legs and settled myself down to wait. I was wretchedly damp and cold, but I tried to cheer myself with the reflection that modern science prescribed open windows and walks in all weather for my disease. Gradually, lulled by the monotonous gurgle of the stream, and by the absolute darkness, I sank into an uneasy slumber[32].

How long this lasted I cannot say. It may have been for an hour, it may have been for several. Suddenly I sat up on my rock couch, with every nerve thrilling and every sense acutely on the alert. Beyond all doubt I had heard a sound – some sound very distinct from the gurgling of the waters. It had passed, but the reverberation of it still lingered in my ear. Was it a search party? They would most certainly have shouted, and vague as this sound was which had wakened me, it was very distinct from the human voice. I sat palpitating and hardly daring to breathe. There it was again! And again! Now it had become continuous. It was a tread – yes, surely it was the tread of some living creature. But what a tread it was! It gave one the impression of enormous weight carried upon sponge-like feet, which gave forth a muffled but ear-filling sound. The darkness was as complete as ever, but the tread was regular and decisive. And it was coming beyond all question in my direction.

31 *old-fashioned*: drink
32 *old-fashioned*: sleep

My skin grew cold, and my hair stood on end as I listened to that steady and ponderous[33] footfall. There was some creature there, and surely by the speed of its advance, it was one which could see in the dark. I crouched low on my rock and tried to blend myself into it. The steps grew nearer still, then stopped, and presently I was aware of a loud lapping and gurgling. The creature was drinking at the stream. Then again there was silence, broken by a succession of long sniffs and snorts of tremendous volume and energy. Had it caught the scent of me? My own nostrils were filled by a low fetid odour, mephitic[34] and abominable[35]. Then I heard the steps again. They were on my side of the stream now. The stones rattled within a few yards of where I lay. Hardly daring to breathe, I crouched upon my rock. Then the steps drew away. I heard the splash as it returned across the river, and the sound died away into the distance in the direction from which it had come.

For a long time I lay upon the rock, too much horrified to move. I thought of the sound which I had heard coming from the depths of the cave, of Armitage's fears, of the strange impression in the mud, and now came this final and absolute proof that there was indeed some inconceivable monster, something utterly unearthly and dreadful, which lurked in the hollow of the mountain. Of its nature or form I could frame no conception[36], save[37] that it was both light-footed and gigantic. The combat between my reason, which told me that such things could not be, and my senses, which told me that they were, raged within me as I lay. Finally, I was almost ready to persuade myself that this experience had been part of some evil dream, and that my abnormal condition might have conjured up an hallucination[38]. But there remained one final experience which removed the last possibility of doubt from my mind.

I had taken my matches from my armpit and felt them. They

33 *mainly literary:* slow and heavy
34 *old-fashioned:* a bad, and possibly poisonous, smell
35 *formal:* terrible, hateful
36 *old-fashioned, phrase 'frame no conception':* form any idea
37 *old-fashioned:* except
38 the initial 'h' is sounded in modern English, a hallucination

seemed perfectly hard and dry. Stooping down into a crevice of the rocks, I tried one of them. To my delight it took fire at once. I lit the candle, and, with a terrified backward glance into the obscure depths of the cavern, I hurried in the direction of the Roman passage. As I did so I passed the patch of mud on which I had seen the huge imprint. Now I stood astonished before it, for there were three similar imprints upon its surface, enormous in size, irregular in outline, of a depth which indicated the ponderous weight which had left them. Then a great terror surged over me. Stooping and shading my candle with my hand, I ran in a frenzy of fear to the rocky archway, hastened up it, and never stopped until, with weary feet and panting lungs, I rushed up the final slope of stones, broke through the tangle of briars, and flung myself exhausted upon the soft grass under the peaceful light of the stars. It was three in the morning when I reached the farm-house, and today I am all unstrung[39] and quivering after my terrific adventure. As yet I have told no one. I must move warily in the matter. What would the poor lonely women, or the uneducated yokels[40] here think of it if I were to tell them my experience? Let me go to someone who can understand and advise.

April 25. I was laid up in bed for two days after my incredible adventure in the cavern. I use the adjective with a very definite meaning, for I have had an experience since which has shocked me almost as much as the other. I have said that I was looking round for someone who could advise me. There is a Dr. Mark Johnson who practises some few miles away, to whom I had a note of recommendation from Professor Saunderson. To him I drove, when I was strong enough to get about, and I recounted[41] to him my whole strange experience. He listened intently, and then carefully examined me, paying special attention to my reflexes and to the pupils of my eyes. When he had finished, he refused to discuss my adventure, saying that it was entirely

39 emotionally upset (CJ not old-fashioned – but not in the MED)
40 *old-fashioned:* simple, uneducated, country people, currently considered impolite
41 *formal:* told

beyond him, but he gave me the card of a Mr. Picton at Castleton, with the advice that I should instantly go to him and tell him the story exactly as I had done to himself. He was, according to my adviser, the very man who was pre-eminently suited to help me. I went on to the station, therefore, and made my way to the little town, which is some ten miles away. Mr. Picton appeared to be a man of importance, as his brass plate was displayed upon the door of a considerable building on the outskirts of the town. I was about to ring his bell, when some misgiving came into my mind, and, crossing to a neighbouring shop, I asked the man behind the counter if he could tell me anything of Mr. Picton. 'Why,' said he, 'he is the best mad doctor in Derbyshire, and yonder[42] is his asylum.' You can imagine that it was not long before I had shaken the dust of Castleton from my feet and returned to the farm, cursing all unimaginative pedants who cannot conceive that there may be things in creation which have never yet chanced to come across their mole's vision. After all, now that I am cooler, I can afford to admit that I have been no more sympathetic to Armitage than Dr. Johnson has been to me.

———

April 27. When I was a student I had the reputation of being a man of courage and enterprise. I remember that when there was a ghost-hunt at Coltbridge it was I who sat up in the haunted house. Is it advancing years (after all, I am only thirty-five), or is it this physical malady[43] which has caused degeneration? Certainly my heart quails[44] when I think of that horrible cavern in the hill, and the certainty that it has some monstrous occupant. What shall I do? There is not an hour in the day that I do not debate the question. If I say nothing, then the mystery remains unsolved. If I do say anything, then I have the alternative of mad alarm over the whole countryside, or of absolute incredulity which may end in consigning me to an asylum. On the whole, I think that my best course is to wait, and to prepare for some expedition which

42 *old-fashioned:* over there
43 *old-fashioned:* illness
44 *literary:* feels very afraid

shall be more deliberate and better thought out than the last. As a first step I have been to Castleton and obtained a few essentials – a large acetylene[45] lantern for one thing, and a good double-barrelled sporting rifle for another. The latter I have hired, but I have bought a dozen heavy game cartridges, which would bring down a rhinoceros. Now I am ready for my troglodyte[46] friend. Give me better health and a little spate of energy, and I shall try conclusions with[47] him yet. But who and what is he? Ah! there is the question which stands between me and my sleep. How many theories do I form, only to discard[48] each in turn[49]! It is all so utterly unthinkable. And yet the cry, the footmark, the tread in the cavern – no reasoning can get past these. I think of the old-world legends of dragons and of other monsters. Were they, perhaps, not such fairy tales as we have thought? Can it be that there is some fact which underlies them, and am I, of all mortals[50], the one who is chosen to expose it?

————

May 3. For several days I have been laid up by the vagaries[51] of an English spring, and during those days there have been developments, the true and sinister meaning of which no one can appreciate save myself. I may say that we have had cloudy and moonless nights of late[52], which according to my information were the seasons upon which sheep disappeared. Well, sheep have disappeared. Two of Miss Allerton's, one of old Pearson's of the Cat Walk, and one of Mrs. Moulton's. Four in all during three nights. No trace is left of them at all, and the countryside is buzzing with rumours of gipsies and of sheep-stealers.

But there is something more serious than that. Young Armitage has disappeared also. He left his moorland cottage early on Wednesday night and has never been heard of since.

45 *technical:* a gas burned with oxygen to produce a flame
46 *old-fashioned:* creature that lives in a cave
47 *old-fashioned, phrase 'try conclusions with':* confront someone
48 *formal:* throw away, dispose of
49 phrase 'in turn': one by one
50 *mainly literary:* people
51 *formal:* unexpected changes that you cannot control
52 *formal phrase 'of late':* recently

He was an unattached man, so there is less sensation than would otherwise be the case. The popular explanation is that he owes money, and has found a situation[53] in some other part of the country, whence[54] he will presently write for his belongings. But I have grave misgivings. Is it not much more likely that the recent tragedy of those sheep has caused him to take some steps which may have ended in his own destruction? He may, for example, have lain in wait for the creature and been carried off by it into the recesses of the mountains. What an inconceivable fate for a civilized Englishman of the twentieth century! And yet I feel that it is possible and even probable. But in that case, how far am I answerable both for his death and for any other mishap which may occur? Surely with the knowledge I already possess it must be my duty to see that something is done, or if necessary to do it myself. It must be the latter, for this morning I went down to the local police-station and told my story. The inspector entered it all in a large book and bowed me out[55] with commendable gravity, but I heard a burst of laughter before I had got down his garden path. No doubt he was recounting my adventure to his family.

June 10. I am writing this, propped up in bed, six weeks after my last entry in this journal. I have gone through a terrible shock both to mind and body, arising from such an experience as has seldom befallen[56] a human being before. But I have attained my end. The danger from the Terror which dwells in the Blue John Gap has passed never to return. Thus much at least I, a broken invalid, have done for the common good. Let me now recount what occurred as clearly as I may.

The night of Friday, May 3rd, was dark and cloudy – the very night for the monster to walk. About eleven o'clock I went from the farm-house with my lantern and my rifle, having first left a note upon the table of my bedroom in which I said that, if I

---

53 *formal*: job
54 *old-fashioned*: from which
55 *old-fashioned, phrase 'bowed me out'*: accompanied politely to the door
56 *literary*: happened to

were missing, search should be made for me in the direction of the Gap. I made my way to the mouth of the Roman shaft, and, having **perched** myself among the rocks close to the opening, I shut off my lantern and waited patiently with my loaded rifle ready to my hand.

It was a melancholy vigil. All down the winding valley I could see the scattered lights of the farm-houses, and the church clock of Chapel-le-Dale tolling the hours came faintly to my ears. These tokens of my fellow-men served only to make my own position seem the more lonely, and to call for a greater effort to overcome the terror which tempted me continually to get back to the farm, and abandon for ever this dangerous quest. And yet there lies deep in every man a rooted self-respect which makes it hard for him to turn back from that which he has once undertaken. This feeling of personal pride was my salvation now, and it was that alone which held me fast when every instinct of my nature was dragging me away. I am glad now that I had the strength. In spite of all that is has cost me, my manhood is at least above reproach.

Twelve o'clock struck in the distant church, then one, then two. It was the darkest hour of the night. The clouds were drifting low, and there was not a star in the sky. An owl was hooting somewhere among the rocks, but no other sound, save the gentle sough[57] of the wind, came to my ears. And then suddenly I heard it! From far away down the tunnel came those muffled steps, so soft and yet so ponderous. I heard also the rattle of stones as they gave way under that giant tread. They drew nearer. They were close upon me. I heard the crashing of the bushes round the entrance, and then dimly through the darkness I was conscious of the loom of some enormous shape, some monstrous inchoate[58] creature, passing swiftly and very silently out from the tunnel. I was paralysed with fear and amazement. Long as I had waited, now that it had actually come I was unprepared for the shock. I lay motionless and breathless, whilst the great dark mass whisked by me and was swallowed up in the night.

57 *old-fashioned:* sigh
58 *very formal:* just beginning to develop or form

But now I nerved[59] myself for its return. No sound came from the sleeping countryside to tell of the horror which was loose. In no way could I judge how far off it was, what it was doing, or when it might be back. But not a second time should my nerve fail me, not a second time should it pass unchallenged. I swore it between my clenched teeth as I laid my cocked rifle across the rock.

And yet it nearly happened. There was no warning of approach now as the creature passed over the grass. Suddenly, like a dark, drifting shadow, the huge bulk loomed up once more before me, making for the entrance of the cave. Again came that paralysis of volition[60] which held my crooked forefinger impotent[61] upon the trigger. But with a desperate effort I shook it off. Even as the brushwood rustled, and the monstrous beast blended with the shadow of the Gap, I fired at the retreating form. In the blaze of the gun I caught a glimpse of a great shaggy mass, something with rough and bristling hair of a withered grey colour, fading away to white in its lower parts, the huge body supported upon short, thick, curving legs. I had just that glance, and then I heard the rattle of the stones as the creature tore down into its burrow. In an instant, with a triumphant revulsion of feeling, I had cast my fears to the wind, and uncovering my powerful lantern, with my rifle in my hand, I sprang down from my rock and rushed after the monster down the old Roman shaft.

My splendid lamp cast a brilliant flood of vivid light in front of me, very different from the yellow glimmer which had aided me down the same passage only twelve days before. As I ran, I saw the great beast lurching along before me, its huge bulk filling up the whole space from wall to wall. Its hair looked like coarse faded oakum[62], and hung down in long, dense masses which swayed as it moved. It was like an enormous unclipped sheep in its fleece, but in size it was far larger than the largest elephant, and its breadth seemed to be nearly as great as its height. It

59 *old-fashioned:* steadied my nerves
60 *formal:* the power or ability to take action
61 *formal:* still, useless, unable to function/move
62 fibre from old ropes

fills me with amazement now to think that I should have dared to follow such a horror into the bowels of the earth, but when one's blood is up, and when one's quarry seems to be flying, the old primeval hunting-spirit awakes and prudence is cast to the wind. Rifle in hand, I ran at the top of my speed upon the trail of the monster.

I had seen that the creature was swift. Now I was to find out to my cost that it was also very cunning. I had imagined that it was in panic flight, and that I had only to pursue it. The idea that it might turn upon me never entered my excited brain. I have already explained that the passage down which I was racing opened into a great central cave. Into this I rushed, fearful lest[63] I should lose all trace of the beast. But he had turned upon his own traces, and in a moment we were face to face.

That picture, seen in the brilliant white light of the lantern, is etched for ever upon my brain. He had reared up on his hind legs as a bear would do, and stood above me, enormous, menacing – such a creature as no nightmare had ever brought to my imagination. I have said that he reared like a bear, and there was something bear-like – if one could conceive a bear which was ten-fold the bulk of any bear seen upon earth – in his whole pose and attitude, in his great crooked forelegs with their ivory-white claws, in his rugged skin, and in his red, gaping mouth, fringed with monstrous fangs. Only in one point did he differ from the bear, or from any other creature which walks the earth, and even at that supreme moment a shudder of horror passed over me as I observed that the eyes which glistened in the glow of my lantern were huge, projecting bulbs, white and sightless. For a moment his great paws swung over my head. The next he fell forward upon me, I and my broken lantern crashed to the earth, and I remember no more.

When I came to myself I was back in the farm-house of the Allertons. Two days had passed since my terrible adventure in the Blue John Gap. It seems that I had lain all night in the cave insensible[64] from concussion of the brain, with my left arm

63 *formal:* in case
64 *formal:* unconscious

and two ribs badly fractured. In the morning my note had been found, a search party of a dozen farmers assembled, and I had been **tracked down** and carried back to my bedroom, where I had lain in high delirium ever since. There was, it seems, no sign of the creature, and no bloodstain which would show that my bullet had found him as he passed. Save for my own plight and the marks upon the mud, there was nothing to prove that what I said was true.

Six weeks have now elapsed[65], and I am able to sit out once more in the sunshine. Just opposite me is the steep hillside, grey with shaly rock, and yonder on its flank is the dark cleft which marks the opening of the Blue John Gap. But it is no longer a source of terror. Never again through that ill-omened tunnel shall any strange shape flit out into the world of men. The educated and the scientific, the Dr. Johnsons and the like, may smile at my narrative, but the poorer folk of the countryside had never a doubt as to its truth. On the day after my recovering consciousness they assembled in their hundreds round the Blue John Gap. As the Castleton Courier said:

'It was useless for our correspondent, or for any of the adventurous gentlemen who had come from Matlock, Buxton, and other parts, to offer to descend, to explore the cave to the end, and to finally test the extraordinary narrative of Dr. James Hardcastle. The country people had taken the matter into their own hands, and from an early hour of the morning they had worked hard in stopping up the entrance of the tunnel. There is a sharp slope where the shaft begins, and great boulders, rolled along by many willing hands, were thrust down it until the Gap was absolutely sealed. So ends the episode which has caused such excitement throughout the country. Local opinion is fiercely divided upon the subject. On the one hand are those who point to Dr. Hardcastle's impaired health, and to the possibility of cerebral lesions of tubercular origin giving rise to strange hallucinations. Some idee fixe[66], according to these gentlemen, caused the doctor to wander down the tunnel,

65 *formal:* passed
66 *French, phrase 'idee fixe':* obsession

and a fall among the rocks was sufficient to account for his injuries. On the other hand, a legend of a strange creature in the Gap has existed for some months back, and the farmers look upon Dr. Hardcastle's narrative and his personal injuries as a final corroboration. So the matter stands, and so the matter will continue to stand, for no definite solution seems to us to be now possible. It transcends human wit[67] to give any scientific explanation which could cover the alleged facts.'

Perhaps before the Courier published these words they would have been wise to send their representative to me. I have thought the matter out[68], as no one else has occasion to do, and it is possible that I might have removed some of the more obvious difficulties of the narrative and brought it one degree nearer to scientific acceptance. Let me then write down the only explanation which seems to me to elucidate[69] what I know to my cost to have been a series of facts. My theory may seem to be wildly improbable, but at least no one can venture to say that it is impossible.

My view is – and it was formed, as is shown by my diary, before my personal adventure – that in this part of England there is a vast subterranean lake or sea, which is fed by the great number of streams which pass down through the limestone. Where there is a large collection of water there must also be some evaporation, mists or rain, and a possibility of vegetation. This in turn suggests that there may be animal life, arising, as the vegetable life would also do, from those seeds and types which had been introduced at an early period of the world's history, when communication with the outer air was more easy. This place had then developed a fauna and flora of its own, including such monsters as the one which I had seen, which may well have been the old cave-bear, enormously enlarged and modified by its new environment. For countless aeons[70] the internal and the external creation had kept apart, growing steadily away from each other. Then there

67 *formal*: intelligence
68 *old-fashioned*: in modern English we would use the prepositions *over* or *through*
69 *formal*: explain
70 *old-fashioned*: an extremely long period of time

had come some rift in the depths of the mountain which had enabled one creature to wander up and, by means of the Roman tunnel, to reach the open air. Like all subterranean life, it had lost the power of sight, but this had no doubt been compensated for by nature in other directions. Certainly it had some means of finding its way about, and of hunting down the sheep upon the hillside. As to its choice of dark nights, it is part of my theory that light was painful to those great white eyeballs, and that it was only a pitch-black world which it could tolerate. Perhaps, indeed, it was the glare of my lantern which saved my life at that awful moment when we were face to face. So I read the **riddle**. I leave these facts behind me, and if you can explain them, do so; or if you choose to doubt them, do so. Neither your belief nor your incredulity can alter them, nor affect one whose task is nearly over.

So ended the strange narrative of Dr. James Hardcastle.

Post-reading exercises

Understanding the story

1 Use these questions to help you check that you have understood the story. Who is introducing the story? Why?

April 17

Look at the conversation between Hardcastle and Armitage.

1 What evidence does Armitage offer for the monster's existence?
2 How does Hardcastle explain the circumstances, to show that it is not a monster?
3 What makes Hardcastle curious to find out more?

April 20

4 Why doesn't Hardcastle tell the Allerton sisters that he has been exploring the Blue John Gap?
5 What makes him think the story might be true, or partly true?
6 Is his attitude purely scientific?

April 22

7 What did Hardcastle see in the mud on his way in?
8 What did he think it might be?
9 How long did he wait in the dark?
10 What exactly did he hear and feel?
11 What did he see in the mud as he left?

April 25

12 Why did Hardcastle visit Dr Johnson?
13 What did Dr Johnson do? Why?
14 Did Hardcastle understand why Dr Johnson sent him to see *the best mad doctor in Derbyshire*? Why/why not?

April 27

15 Why didn't Hardcastle tell anyone else about his adventure?
16 Why did he decide to go back to the cave?

May 3

17 Why did Hardcastle go to the police?
18 How did the inspector react? Why?

June 10

19 Where did Hardcastle wait for the monster? Why?
20 How did he feel as he chased the monster down the passage?
21 What was the last thing he remembered?

22 Where was he when he woke up?
23 How did they rescue him?
24 What did the locals do to the entrance to Blue John Gap? Why?
25 How does the newspaper explain the story?
26 What is Hardcastle's explanation?
27 Do you think it is scientifically possible?

Language study

Dr Hardcastle is a scientist. He is a wealthy and educated man and his written style, even in his personal diary, reflects this. His descriptions are full of scientific details and his language is often very formal, both in the grammatical structures and the vocabulary he uses.

Grammar

Creating emphasis[71]: inversion after negative and limiting adverbials

One way of creating emphasis is to put an adverb at the beginning of a sentence. When the adverb has a negative or limiting meaning, we have to change the order of the subject and the verb – this is called inversion. This structure is very formal and usually only used in writing.

1 **Look at these examples from the story. Notice the inversion of the subject and verb.**

   *Only then **did I realise** my position.*
   *In no way **could I judge** how far off it was.*
   *Not a second time **should my nerve fail** me.*
   *Only in one point **did he differ** from a bear.*

2 **Complete the sentences below so that they mean the same as the sentences in the story.**

1 I only .... then (at that moment).
2 There was no way ....
3 My nerve .... a second time.
4 He .... from the bear in one point (way).

3 **Which sentences are more emphatic, those in the story or the sentences you wrote? What is the author emphasising?**

---

71 special importance that is given to one thing in particular

4 Rewrite the sentences, using the adverbs given.

1 He had never heard such a terrible sound.
Never ...

2 He had never seen such a terrible sight before.
Never before ...

3 There was no way the locals were going to risk the monster reappearing.
In no way ...

4 It was not until then that he saw the monster's eyes.
Only then ...

5 He didn't know what he was going to find.
Little ...

6 He had seldom felt so vulnerable and alone.
Seldom ...

Prepositions in relative clauses

In everyday modern usage when we use prepositions with a relative pronoun (who, which, that) the preposition comes at the end of the sentence.

> *The story **that** I was telling you **about**.*
> *The area **which** Hardcastle was staying **in**.*
> *The man **who** he told his story **to**.*

Notice how Hardcastle uses prepositions in relative clauses.

> *the black depths **into which** I peered*
> *a curious rock formation **by which** I could recognise the entrance*
> *the sound died away in the direction **from which** it had come*
> *Dr. Mark Johnson, **to whom** I had a note of recommendation*

He puts the preposition directly in front of the pronoun. When the pronoun is *who* it changes to *whom*. This structure is very formal, and usually only found in formal, written texts. It can make a text sound old-fashioned if it is used too much.

5 Rewrite the extracts from the story. Put the prepositions at the end of the sentence.

1 The black depths .... I peered ....
2 A curious rock formation .... I could recognise the entrance
....
3 The sound died away in the direction .... it had come ....
4 Dr. Mark Johnson, ... I had a note of recommendation ....

Use of the pronoun *one*

Hardcastle often uses the pronoun *one* instead of *you* when he is talking about something that happens to people in general, including himself. He also uses it, at times, instead of *I* or *me*, to talk about himself, in a less personal way. Both uses make him sound formal and old-fashioned.[72]

Look at these examples. Notice how *one* can be used as a subject pronoun, an object pronoun or with the possessive *'s*.

1 *it was not a boom, nor a crash, such as* **one** *would associate with falling water*
2 *in that black, velvety darkness* **one** *lost all* **one's** *bearings in an instant when* **one's** *blood is up, and when* **one's** *quarry seems to be flying*
3 *it gave* **one** *the impression of enormous weight carried upon sponge-like feet*

6 **Rewrite the sentences above, replacing *one* and *one's* with *you*, *your*, *I* or *me*.**

Formal vocabulary

The story contains a lot of formal vocabulary. The very formal vocabulary, which is unusual in modern English, is explained in the footnotes. Other examples of formal vocabulary are not so rare and don't need explanation, but would sound strange if you used them in everyday, spoken English.

Here are some examples.

> *I have made* **several expeditions** *to the Blue John Gap, and have even* **penetrated** *some short distance.*
> *How far am I* **answerable** *both for his death and for any other* **mishap** *which may* **occur***?*
> *The danger from the terror which* **dwells** *in the Blue John Gap has* **passed** *never to* **return.***

7 **Replace the formal words in bold above, with the more frequently used words in the box below.**

accident   a lot of   come back   gone   gone in   happen   lives
responsible   visits

---

72 this use of *one* is still quite widely used by the upper classes and intellectuals

Multiple-clause sentences

One of the features of an authentic text is the variety in sentence length. Some of the sentences in the story are very short – perhaps only three or four words. They are often used to create dramatic effect:

> *They drew nearer.*
> *There it was again!*
> *Well, sheep have disappeared.*

Other sentences contain five, six or even seven clauses. Look at this sentence for example. The clauses are numbered:

> *In a instant, (1) with a triumphant revulsion of feeling, (2) I had cast my fears to the wind, and (3) uncovering my powerful lantern, (4) with my rifle in my hand, (5) I sprang down from my rock and (6) rushed after the monster (7) down the old Roman shaft.*

Look at how the clauses break down into short sentences.

I felt a triumphant revulsion of feeling.
I cast my fears to the wind.
I uncovered my powerful lantern.
I held my rifle in my hand.
I sprang down from my rock.
I rushed after the monster.
I rushed down the old Roman shaft.

In this case, the long sentence, containing all these details and actions, creates a dramatic effect of many things happening all at the same time.

8 **Look at another example. How many clauses are there in this sentence? Use commas to separate the clauses where necessary. Check your answers on page 27.**

> *As I rose from the examination of that singular mark and then looked round into the black shadows which hemmed me in I must confess that I felt for a moment a most unpleasant sinking of my heart and that do what I could the candle trembled in my outstretched hand.*

9 **Now break the sentence down into five, or more, separate sentences. Compare your sentences to the one in the story. What is the difference in the effect?**

You will find examples of multiple-clause sentences throughout your reading of authentic texts. In this book, you will see many examples. Sentences like this are usually used to create atmosphere, or to change the pace of the story. It can be very effective but the length and complexity of the sentences can also be confusing. If you find multiple-clause sentences difficult, break down the longer sentences into shorter clauses, as you have done here – this will make it easier to understand.

Literary analysis

Plot

1 What are the main events in the plot? Write a one-sentence summary of the plot.
2 What do you think is the one, most important event? How does the plot lead up to this event? What happens as a consequence of the event? Think about what happens to the Blue John Gap, the reactions in the press, and how Hardcastle chooses to deal with the situation.
3 Do you think Hardcastle really saw a strange creature or was he just hallucinating? Give reasons for your answers.
4 Hardcastle talks a lot about about the gap between superstition and science, and between imagination and reality. What does the story tell us about superstition? What does the story tell us about scepticism?

Character

5 What do you know about Hardcastle? Think about his age, his health, his educational background. Choose three adjectives to describe him.
6 What was his first reaction to the stories about the Terror? What first made him change his mind? What other 'evidence' did he collect?
7 Which characters represent superstition and which represent science? What does Hardcastle represent?
8 Do you think Hardcastle might be going mad? Support your answer with evidence from the story.
9 Hardcastle is described as *a man of sober and scientific turn of mind, almost devoid of imagination, and most unlikely to invent any abnormal series of events*. Do you think this is true? Is he really *devoid of imagination*[73]?
10 What about the role of the monster in the story – what do we know about it? What does it represent?

73 has no imagination

Narration

11　Is Hardcastle a reliable narrator[74]? Can we believe his version of the story? Do you think he is able to be objective?

12　At times, the narrative switches quite quickly from giving scientific details of the facts to describing Hardcastle's emotional reactions. Which do you think dominate the story – the facts or his reactions to the monster?

13　Think about how the story would have been told differently if it had been told by one of the Allerton sisters? Or by Dr Johnston? Think about what they knew of the affair, and what their attitudes would have been, both to Hardcastle and the monster.

Atmosphere

14　What are the main elements that contribute to the suspense and the fear in the story? Think of things like sounds, smells and physical descriptions.

15　Think of the scene when Hardcastle is waiting for the monster at the entrance to the cave. What details in the description make this scene typical of a horror story?

16　Describe the monster. What makes it so terrifying? Are you convinced by the description? Why/why not?

Style

17　Look at the conversation between Hardcastle and Armitage [pages 23–24] and think about these questions.
　　– Why does the author first use direct speech and then change to reported speech? What effect does this have?
　　– Notice the use of the passive (*had been found, could be explained*) and modals of speculation (*could have wandered*). What effect does this create?
　　– Notice how the structure of detail followed by explanation is used throughout all of the reported conversation. What does this tell us about Hardcastle and his attitude to the story?

18　Look at the passage where Hardcastle explains how he came to be lost in the darkness of the underground cave [page 27–28]. Notice how he introduces the incident in the first sentence of the paragraph, before continuing to describe it in detail. Can you think

---

74　a narrator who we can trust, who is telling us the objective truth

of any other examples in the story where he does this? What effect does this have?

19 Look at the same passage and notice how many times he uses the word *darkness* in the first four paragraphs [page 28–29]. Notice the adjectives he uses to describe the darkness. What effect does the darkness have on Hardcastle? How does he describe this effect?

20 Look at the description of Hardcastle's encounter with the monster in the dark [pages 29–30]. Notice how he uses short sentences and exclamations as he describes the sound he hears. Try reading the two paragraphs aloud. What effect does this create? What happens as the creature moves away?

21 Look at the passage where Hardcastle describes the scene as he waits for the monster to come out of the entrance to the Blue John Gap [page 35]. What can he see? What can he hear? What elements in the description are typical of a ghost or horror story?

22 Look at the passage where Hardcastle chases the monster into the cave and finally sees what it looks like [page 36]. Look at the use of long, complex sentences to describe the monster. Notice the comparisons Hardcastle makes as he tries to describe this incredible creature. Notice how Hardcastle first uses the pronoun *it* to talk about the monster, but then switches to *he*. Why does he do this?

Guidance to the above literary terms, answer keys to all the exercises and activities, plus a wealth of other reading-practice material, can be found on the student's section of the Macmillan Readers website at: www.macmillanenglish.com/readers.

Oh, Whistle and I'll Come to You, My Lad
by M R James

About the author

Montague Rhodes James is known as one of the best writers of ghost stories in the English language. He was a scholar and an academic, specialising in history and the classics. He was the Vice Chancellor of King's College, Cambridge, where every Christmas he would read ghost stories to his colleagues and pupils by candlelight.

M R James was born in 1862. His father was an Anglican priest and he grew up in Suffolk, on the east coast of England. Many of his short stories are set in Suffolk, including *Oh, Whistle and I'll Come, My Lad*. He was educated at Eton[1] and then at King's College, Cambridge. After graduating he stayed on at the college, where he spent most of his working life. Towards the end of his career he returned to his old school, Eton College, as Vice Chancellor. He died in 1936 at the age of seventy-three.

M R James was a highly-respected scholar in the field of medieval studies, paleography[2] and Bible studies. He often refers to these fields of study in his stories, and his main characters often share his background and interest in medieval and classical history.

While he was at King's College, M R James became interested in tales of the supernatural[3]. He adapted descriptions of ghosts that he discovered in old documents and papers and read them to his friends. This soon grew into an annual Christmas ghost storytelling event. In 1904, James published his first collection of ghost stories, *Ghost Stories of an Antiquary*. He published a further three collections during his lifetime – more than 20 tales in all. His stories are still published in collections and anthologies today.

His stories have had an enormous influence on other ghost-story writers; in fact, a distinctive genre emerged – the 'Jamesian' story. James's stories include certain key features – a peaceful setting, an

---

1 one of the oldest, most expensive and most respected private schools in the UK
2 the study of ancient manuscripts
3 things which seem to come from a power such as magic, and do not have a natural or scientific explanation

academic as the main character, and an antique object that conjures up[4] a ghost. These features have become a well-known and well-loved formula, elements of all 'Jamesian' stories.

About the story

The story was published in 1904 in James's first collection of ghost stories, *Ghost Stories of an Antiquary*. The title of the story is taken from the title and chorus line of a love poem and song by Robert Burns (1793).

Background information

Burnstow

The story is set in the fictitious[5] seaside town of Burnstow, on the east coast of England. Burnstow is based on the town of Felixstowe, with its windswept golf course on the sea front, and its long grey beach, lined with old, stone groynes (low walls built to protect the beach from waves). A BBC TV production of the story, made in 1968, used Felixstowe as its location.

Whistling

Whistling has traditionally been considered to bring bad luck in a number of cultures. It is also believed to be a way of calling up spirits. At one time, whistling was forbidden on sailing ships, but many believed that some sailors and fishermen knew how to call a wind by whistling.

4 *verb:* to make something appear using magic powers
5 imaginary

Summary

It may help you to know something about what happens in the story before you read it. Don't worry, this summary does not tell you how the story ends!

A university professor is spending a couple of weeks on the coast, improving his golf during his holiday. A colleague has asked him to investigate a possible archaeological site near his hotel.

Returning to his hotel at the end of his first day of golf, the Professor decides to look for the site. He finds it easily and starts to make measurements and take notes. He finds a small, metal object in a small, square hole. He puts the object in his pocket, planning to give it to his colleague at the university.

As he is walking back to his hotel, he notices a strange figure on the beach. It seems to be following him, but never actually catches up with him. Back in his room, after dinner, he remembers the metal object in his pocket. He realises it's a whistle. He cleans it and blows it to see if it works. It does.

As soon as he blows the whistle, a strong wind blows open his window, and he has to fight against the wind to close it again. That night, the wind continues to blow, and the Professor is troubled by strange thoughts, images and sounds.

He tells his golfing partner, the Colonel, about the whistle. The Colonel thinks it is unwise to keep the whistle – thinking perhaps it is connected with the strong wind that was blowing the night before. But the Professor dismisses his superstitions.

When they get back to the hotel, they are met by a boy who has been frightened by a strange figure, whom he saw waving from the Professor's bedroom window. When they investigate, they find no sign of the intruder. The Professor thinks that the boy may have been joking, but the colonel, his golfing partner, is worried.

That night, as the two men go to bed, the colonel is worried that something might happen to the Professor. The Professor does not take his concerns seriously, not realising the horrors the night will bring…

Pre-reading exercises

Key vocabulary

This section will help you familiarise yourself with some of the more specific vocabulary used in the story. You may want to use it to help you before you start reading, or as a revision exercise after you've finished the story.

The archaeological site

The Professor has promised a colleague that he will look for the site of an old church when he is on holiday. He takes his time, and explores the site very carefully. His precise, scholarly approach is reflected in the language he uses to describe it. The author uses specific, or scientific terms to describe its geography and his examination of it.

1 **Look at the extracts below. Match the words in bold with the definitions below.**

> (a) *He found himself in a patch of somewhat **broken ground** covered with small **depressions** and **mounds**. These latter, when he came to examine them, proved to be simply masses of **flints** embedded in **mortar** and grown over with **turf**.*

1 ....a piece of hard grey stone
2 ....a small hill, or pile of stones or earth
3 ....uneven surface – not flat or regular
4 ....short grass
5 ....scientific: an area or surface that is lower than the parts around it
6 ....a substance used in building for holding bricks or stones together

> (b) *It might, he thought, be as well to **probe** the **soil** here for evidences of **masonry**, and he took out his knife and began **scraping** away the earth. And now followed another little discovery: a portion of soil fell inward as he scraped, and disclosed a small **cavity**.*

1 .... to rub a sharp edge or tool against a surface
2 .... to examine
3 .... a hole
4 .... the bricks or stones that make a building
5 .... the substance in which plants grow

2 **Make these sentences more formal or specific by replacing the words in bold with the words in the extracts above.**

1 He **looked carefully** at the pile of sand.
2 He **took** the mud **off** his shoe with a sharp stick.
3 He put his hand against the wall and discovered a **hole**.
4 The rescue team had to climb over **fallen bricks and stones** to get to the victims.
5 As he kicked the ball, a piece of **grass and earth** flew up into his face.
6 In medieval times they used **a mixture of sand, water and lime** to build walls.

Spoken language

The world that James describes has strict class divisions. We can see this in the way the author writes dialogue. The conversations between the scholars at St James's college, and between the Colonel and Parkins, are written in standard English. The speech of the hotel staff and the boy in the garden, however, are not. The writer uses non-standard spelling to convey the local accent and pronunciation of the speakers.

Accent and pronunciation

3 **Look at the words in bold. How would you normally spell them in standard English?**

1 *Beg your pardon, sir, but as I was a-brushing your coat just now there was **somethink** fell out of the pocket.*
2 *I beg your pardon, sir, but you seemed to have tried both of **'em**; leastways, we had to make **'em** both up this morning.*
3 *Ow, I seen it **wive** at me out of the **winder** (wive – hold its hand up and move it about, to say hello or goodbye)*
4 *The front **winder** it was, at the **'otel**.*
5 *The **seckind** one it was – the big winder what got two little **uns** at the sides.*
6 *Mr. Simpson he **kep'** the keys.*

Non-standard English

4 Here are some of the non-standard features that we can see in the speech of the hotel staff. Look at the notes and rewrite the examples on page 53 in standard, current English.

Double negatives

Standard English does not place two negatives together.

For example:
she hadn't no other key

5 How would you write the sentence above in standard English?

Verb agreement

In non-standard English, the verb agreement in the verb *to be* is often different from standard usage.

For example:

it warn't a right thing – not to say not a right person

6 How would you write the sentence above in standard English?

Continuous verbs

In the story, the speakers add the prefix *a-* to the *-ing* form of the verb.

For example:

he happened to look up at the front winder and see it a-wiving at him

but as I was a-brushing your coat just now there was somethink fell out of the pocket

7 How would you write the sentence above in standard English?

Using *what* as a relative pronoun

It is still a common feature of informal, or uneducated speech to misuse what as a relative pronoun.

For example:

the big winder what got two little uns at the sides

8 How would you write the sentence above in standard English?

Main themes

Before you read the story, you may want to think about some of its main themes. The questions will help you think about the story as you're reading it for the first time. There is more discussion of the main themes in the *Literary analysis* section after the story.

Haunted objects

The main subject matter of the story is a haunted object – an antique whistle. When the whistle is disturbed and the Professor removes it from its hiding place, he disturbs a spirit that is associated with it. Haunted objects are common in ghost stories, and particularly so in Jamesian ghost stories. These objects contain psychic (spiritual or ghostly) energy, absorbed from people who used them in the past; this energy can be released when the object is found or moved.

As you read the story, think about the whistle, about where it was found, the people associated with it, and the kind of energy it might have absorbed. Ask yourself the following questions:
– Do you believe that haunted objects might exist?
– What scientific explanation might there be for what happened?

Science versus superstition

The conflict between science and superstition is a theme we saw in the first story in this collection, *The Terror of Blue John Gap*. It is also a classic theme in many stories about the supernatural. The stories feature a sceptical[6] person who experiences a ghost and having to question their beliefs. In this story, Parkins is openly sceptical, and does not believe in ghosts. For most of the story, he tries to explain the signs of the ghost's presence in a rational way.

9 As you read, ask yourself:

a) Who or what does Parkins represent?
b) Why is it important to the story that Parkins is so sure that ghosts do not exist?

---

6 having doubts about something that other people think is right or true

Oh, Whistle and I'll Come to You, My Lad

by M R James

'I SUPPOSE you will be getting away pretty soon, now. Full term is over, Professor,' said a person not in the story to the Professor of Ontography[7], soon after they had sat down next to each other at a feast in the hospitable hall of St. James's College.

The Professor was young, neat, and precise in speech.

'Yes,' he said; 'my friends have been making me **take up** golf this term, and I mean to go to the East Coast – in point of fact to Burnstow – (I dare say you know it) for a week or ten days, to improve my game. I hope to get off tomorrow.'

'Oh, Parkins,' said his neighbour on the other side, 'if you are going to Burnstow, I wish you would look at the site of the Templars'[8] preceptory[9], and let me know if you think it would be any good to have a dig there in the summer.'

———

It was, as you might suppose, a person of antiquarian pursuits who said this, but, since he merely appears in this prologue, there is no need to give his entitlements[10].

'Certainly,' said Parkins, the Professor: 'if you will describe to me whereabouts the site is, I will do my best to give you an idea of **the lie of the land** when I get back; or I could write to you about it, if you would tell me where you are likely to be.'

'Don't trouble to do that, thanks. It's only that I'm thinking of taking my family in that direction in the Long[11], and it occurred to me that, as very few of the English preceptories have ever been properly planned, I might have an opportunity of doing something useful on off-days.'

---

7 a branch of philosophy that deals with the study of existence
8 The Knights Templar, a Christian military order
9 the headquarters of certain orders of Christian knights
10 *old-fashioned:* qualifications
11 the 'long holiday', the summer holiday

The Professor rather sniffed at the idea that planning out a preceptory could be described as useful. His neighbour continued:

'The site – I doubt if there is anything showing above ground – must be down quite close to the beach now. The sea has encroached tremendously, as you know, all along that bit of coast. I should think, from the map, that it must be about three-quarters of a mile from the Globe Inn, at the north end of the town. Where are you going to stay?'

'Well, *at* the Globe Inn, as a matter of fact,' said Parkins; 'I have engaged[12] a room there. I couldn't get in anywhere else; most of the lodging-houses are shut up in winter, it seems; and, as it is, they tell me that the only room of any size I can have is really a double-bedded one, and that they haven't a corner in which to store the other bed, and so on. But I must have a fairly large room, for I am taking some books down, and mean to do a bit of work; and though I don't quite fancy having an empty bed – not to speak of two – in what I may call for the time being my study, I suppose I can manage to rough it[13] for the short time I shall be there.'

'Do you call having an extra bed in your room roughing it, Parkins?' said a bluff person opposite. 'Look here, I shall come down and occupy it for a bit; it'll be company for you.'

The Professor quivered, but managed to laugh in a courteous manner.

'By all means, Rogers; there's nothing I should like better. But I'm afraid you would find it rather dull; you don't play golf, do you?'

'No, thank Heaven!' said rude Mr. Rogers.

'Well, you see, when I'm not writing I shall most likely be out on the links, and that, as I say, would be rather dull for you, I'm afraid.'

'Oh, I don't know! There's certain to be somebody I know in the place; but, of course, if you don't want me, speak the

12 old-fashioned: *booked*
13 informal: *to live without the things you usually live with, for example water or electricity*

word, Parkins; I shan't be offended. Truth, as you always tell us, is never offensive.'

Parkins was, indeed, scrupulously polite and strictly truthful. It is to be feared that Mr. Rogers sometimes practised upon[14] his knowledge of these characteristics. In Parkins's breast there was a conflict now raging, which for a moment or two did not allow him to answer. That interval being over, he said:

'Well, if you want the exact truth, Rogers, I was considering whether the room I speak of would really be large enough to accommodate us both comfortably; and also whether (mind, I shouldn't have said this if you hadn't pressed me) you would not constitute something in the nature of a hindrance to my work.'

Rogers laughed loudly.

'Well done, Parkins!' he said. 'It's all right. I promise not to interrupt your work; don't you disturb yourself about that. No, I won't come if you don't want me; but I thought I should do so nicely to keep the ghosts off.' Here he might have been seen to wink and to **nudge** his next neighbour. Parkins might also have been seen to become pink. 'I beg pardon, Parkins,' Rogers continued; 'I oughtn't to have said that. I forgot you didn't like levity on these topics.'

'Well,' Parkins said, 'as you have mentioned the matter, I freely own that I do *not* like careless talk about what you call ghosts. A man in my position,' he went on, raising his voice a little, 'cannot, I find, be too careful about appearing to sanction the current beliefs on such subjects. As you know, Rogers, or as you ought to know; for I think I have never concealed my views…'

'No, you certainly have not, old man,' put in Rogers *sotto voce*[15].

'…I hold that any semblance, any appearance of concession to the view that such things might exist is equivalent to a renunciation of all that I hold most sacred. But I'm afraid I have not succeeded in securing your attention.'

14 *old-fashioned*: on
15 Latin, meaning *quietly*, or *under his breath*

'Your *undivided* attention, was what Dr. Blimber actually *said*,[(1)][16] Rogers interrupted, with every appearance of an earnest desire for accuracy. 'But I beg your pardon, Parkins: I'm stopping you.'

'No, not at all,' said Parkins. 'I don't remember Blimber; perhaps he was before my time. But I needn't go on. I'm sure you know what I mean.'

'Yes, yes,' said Rogers, rather hastily. 'Just so. We'll go into it fully at Burnstow, or somewhere.'

In repeating the above dialogue I have tried to give the impression which it made on me, that Parkins was something of an old woman – rather henlike, perhaps, in his little ways; totally destitute, alas![17] of the[18] sense of humour, but at the same time dauntless and sincere in his convictions, and a man deserving of the greatest respect. Whether or not the reader has gathered so much, that was the character which Parkins had.

———

On the following day Parkins did, as he had hoped, succeed in getting away from his college, and in arriving at Burnstow. He was made welcome at the Globe Inn, was safely installed in the large double-bedded room of which we have heard, and was able before retiring to rest to arrange his materials for work in apple-pie order upon a commodious table which occupied the outer end of the room, and was surrounded on three sides by windows looking out seaward; that is to say, the central window looked straight out to sea, and those on the left and right commanded prospects along the shore to the north and south respectively. On the south you saw the village of Burnstow. On the north no houses were to be seen, but only the beach and the low cliff backing it. Immediately in front was a strip – not considerable – of rough grass, dotted with old anchors, capstans[19], and so forth;

(1) Mr. Rogers was wrong, *vide Dombey and Son*, chapter xii

16 this footnote is included in the original story and refers to the fact that Rogers is mistaken in his reference to Charles Dickens's novel, *Dombie and Son*

17 *old-fashioned:* unfortunately

18 an article would not be necessary here in current usage

19 *technical:* a round piece of equipment that you turn to wind a heavy rope, especially on a ship or at a port

then a broad path; then the beach. Whatever may have been the original distance between the Globe Inn and the sea, not more than sixty yards now separated them.

The rest of the population of the inn was, of course, a golfing one, and included few elements that call for a special description. The most conspicuous figure was, perhaps, that of an *ancien militaire*[20] secretary of a London club[21], and possessed of a voice of incredible strength, and of views of a pronouncedly Protestant type. These were apt to find utterance after his attendance upon the ministrations of the Vicar[22], an estimable man with inclinations towards a picaresque[23] ritual, which he gallantly kept down as far as he could out of deference to East Anglian[24] tradition.

Professor Parkins, one of whose principal characteristics was pluck[25], spent the greater part of the day following his arrival at Burnstow in what he had called improving his game, in company with this Colonel Wilson: and during the afternoon – whether the process of improvement were to blame or not, I am not sure – the Colonel's demeanour assumed a colouring so lurid that even Parkins jibbed at[26] the thought of walking home with him from the links. He determined[27], after a short and furtive look at that bristling moustache and those incarnadined[28] features, that it would be wiser to allow the influences of tea and tobacco to do what they could with the Colonel before the dinner-hour should render a meeting inevitable.

'I might walk home to-night along the beach,' he reflected – 'yes, and take a look – there will be light enough for that – at the ruins of which Disney was talking. I don't exactly know where they are, by the way; but I expect I can hardly help stumbling[29] on them.'

20 *French:* a retired military officer
21 a private social club for upper-class men
22 a priest in the church of England
23 exciting, easy to like, despite not being very moral or honest
24 from East Anglia, a region in the south east of England
25 *old-fashioned:* courage
26 *phrasal verb, old-fashioned:* to be unwilling to do something
27 *formal:* decided
28 *old-fashioned, formal:* red
29 falling over something as you walk

This he accomplished, I may say, in the most literal sense, for in picking his way from the links to the shingle beach his foot caught, partly in a gorse[30]-root and partly in a biggish stone, and over he went. When he got up and surveyed his surroundings, he found himself in a patch of somewhat broken ground covered with small depressions and mounds. These latter, when he came to examine them, proved to be simply masses of flints embedded in mortar and grown over with turf. He must, he quite rightly concluded, be on the site of the preceptory he had promised to look at. It seemed not unlikely to reward the spade of the explorer; enough of the foundations was probably left at no great depth to throw a good deal of light on the general plan. He remembered vaguely that the Templars, to whom this site had belonged, were in the habit of building round churches, and he thought a particular series of the humps or mounds near him did appear to be arranged in something of a circular form. Few people can resist the temptation to try a little amateur research in a department quite outside their own, if only for the satisfaction of showing how successful they would have been had they only taken it up seriously. Our Professor, however, if he felt something of this mean desire, was also truly anxious to oblige Mr. Disney. So he paced with care the circular area he had noticed, and wrote down its rough dimensions in his pocket-book. Then he proceeded to examine an oblong eminence[31] which lay east of the centre of the circle, and seemed to his thinking likely to be the base of a platform or altar. At one end of it, the northern, a patch of the turf was gone – removed by some boy or other creature *feræ naturæ*[32]. It might, he thought, be as well to probe the soil here for evidences of masonry, and he took out his knife and began scraping away the earth. And now followed another little discovery: a portion of soil fell inward as he scraped, and disclosed a small cavity. He lighted[33] one match after another to help him to see of what nature the hole was, but the wind was too strong for them all. By tapping and scratching the sides with

30 a small bush that has yellow flowers
31 *old-fashioned, formal*: something that sticks out above something else
32 *Latin*: wild, not domesticated
33 in current English the past simple form of *light* is *lit*

his knife, however, he was able to make out that it must be an artificial hole in masonry. It was rectangular, and the sides, top, and bottom, if not actually plastered, were smooth and regular. Of course it was empty. No! As he withdrew the knife he heard a metallic clink, and when he introduced his hand it met with a cylindrical object lying on the floor of the hole. Naturally enough, he picked it up, and when he brought it into the light, now fast fading, he could see that it, too, was of man's making – a metal tube about four inches long, and evidently of some considerable age.

By the time Parkins had made sure that there was nothing else in this odd receptacle, it was too late and too dark for him to think of undertaking any further search. What he had done had proved so unexpectedly interesting that he determined to sacrifice a little more of the daylight on the morrow[34] to archaeology. The object which he now had safe in his pocket was bound to be of some slight value at least, he felt sure.

Bleak and solemn was the view on which he took a last look before starting homeward. A faint yellow light in the west showed the links, on which a few figures moving towards the club-house were still visible, the squat martello tower[35], the lights of Aldsey village, the pale ribbon of sands intersected at intervals by black wooden groynes[36], the dim and murmuring sea. The wind was bitter from the north, but was at his back when he set out for the Globe. He quickly rattled and clashed through the shingle and gained the sand, upon which, but for the groynes which had to be got over every few yards, the going was both good and quiet. One last look behind, to measure the distance he had made since leaving the ruined Templars' church, showed him a prospect of company on his walk, in the shape of a rather indistinct personage[37], who seemed to be making great efforts to catch up with him, but made little, if any, progress. I mean that there was

34 *old-fashioned*: the next day
35 short, circular towers made of brick, built for defense purposes during the Napoleonic Wars in the early 19th century
36 a low wall, built on the sand, pointing out to sea, used to protect beaches from being damaged by waves
37 *formal*: character in a play, film or book

an appearance of running about his movements, but that the distance between him and Parkins did not seem materially to lessen. So, at least, Parkins thought, and decided that he almost certainly did not know him, and that it would be absurd to wait until he came up. For all that, company, he began to think, would really be very welcome on that lonely shore, if only you could choose your companion. In his unenlightened days he had read of meetings in such places which even now would hardly bear thinking of. He went on thinking of them, however, until he reached home, and particularly of one which catches most people's fancy at some time of their childhood. 'Now I saw in my dream that Christian had gone but a very little way when he saw a foul fiend coming over the field to meet him.'[38] 'What should I do now,' he thought, 'if I looked back and **caught sight of** a black figure sharply defined against the yellow sky, and saw that it had horns and wings? I wonder whether I should stand or run for it. Luckily, the gentleman behind is not of that kind, and he seems to be about as far off now as when I saw him first. Well, at this rate he won't get his dinner as soon as I shall; and, dear me! it's within a quarter of an hour of the time now. I must run!'

Parkins had, in fact, very little time for dressing. When he met the Colonel at dinner, Peace – or as much of her as that gentleman could manage – reigned once more in the military bosom; nor was she put to flight in the hours of bridge[39] that followed dinner, for Parkins was a more than respectable player. When, therefore, he retired towards twelve o'clock, he felt that he had spent his evening in quite a satisfactory way, and that, even for so long as a fortnight or three weeks, life at the Globe would be supportable under similar conditions – 'especially,' thought he, 'if I go on improving my game.'

As he went along the passages he met the boots[40] of the Globe, who stopped and said:

'Beg your pardon, sir, but as I was a-brushing your coat just

38 a reference to John Bunyan's *The Pilgrim's Progress*, a classic of English literature, published in 1678
39 a card game for four players who make two teams
40 *old-fashioned:* a man servant at the hotel

now there was somethink fell out of the pocket. I put it on your chest of drawers, sir in your room, sir – a piece of a pipe or somethink of that, sir. Thank you, sir. You'll find it on your chest of drawers, sir – yes, sir. Good night, sir.'

The speech served to remind Parkins of his little discovery of that afternoon. It was with some considerable curiosity that he turned it over by the light of his candles. It was of bronze, he now saw, and was shaped very much after the manner of the modern dog-whistle; in fact it was – yes, certainly it was – actually no more nor less than a whistle. He put it to his lips, but it was quite full of a fine, caked-up sand or earth, which would not yield to knocking, but must be loosened with a knife. Tidy as ever in his habits, Parkins cleared out the earth on to a piece of paper, and took the latter to the window to empty it out. The night was clear and bright, as he saw when he had opened the casement, and he stopped for an instant to look at the sea and note a belated[41] wanderer stationed on the shore in front of the inn. Then he shut the window, a little surprised at the late hours people kept at Burnstow, and took his whistle to the light again. Why, surely there were marks on it, not merely marks, but letters! A very little rubbing rendered the deeply-cut inscription quite legible, but the Professor had to confess, after some earnest thought, that the meaning of it was as obscure to him as the writing on the wall to Belshazzar[42]. There were legends[43] both on the front and on the back of the whistle. The one read thus:

FLA

FUR FLE

BIS

The other:

卐 QUIS EST ISTE QUI UENIT 卐[44]

---

41 *formal:* late

42 Belshazzar was the son of the last king of Babylon. According to the Biblical story, while Belshazzar and his court were having a feast, a mysterious hand wrote a message on the wall. Belshazzar could not read the writing and had to ask a servant to translate it. The writing warned Belshazzar of his imminent defeat and death

43 *old-fashioned:* a short piece of writing on an object such as an old coin or work of art

44 the swastika was commonly used as a decorative symbol in medieval churches

'I ought to be able to make it out,' he thought; 'but I suppose I am a little rusty in my Latin. When I come to think of it, I don't believe I even know the word for a whistle. The long one does seem simple enough. It ought to mean, "Who is this who is coming?" Well, the best way to find out is evidently to whistle for him.'

He blew tentatively and stopped suddenly, startled and yet pleased at the note he had elicited. It had a quality of infinite distance in it, and, soft as it was, he somehow felt it must be audible for miles round. It was a sound, too, that seemed to have the power (which many scents possess) of forming pictures in the brain. He saw quite clearly for a moment a vision of a wide, dark expanse at night, with a fresh wind blowing, and in the midst[45] a lonely figure – how employed, he could not tell. Perhaps he would have seen more had not the picture been broken by the sudden surge of a gust of wind against his casement, so sudden that it made him look up, just in time to see the white glint of a sea-bird's wing somewhere outside the dark panes. The sound of the whistle had so fascinated him that he could not help trying it once more, this time more boldly. The note was little, if at all, louder than before, and repetition broke the illusion – no picture followed, as he had half hoped it might. 'But what is this? Goodness! what force the wind can get up in a few minutes! What a tremendous gust[46]! There! I knew that window-fastening was no use! Ah! I thought so – both candles out. It's enough to tear the room to pieces.'

The first thing was to get the window shut. While you might count twenty Parkins was struggling with the small casement, and felt almost as if he were pushing back a sturdy burglar, so strong was the pressure. It slackened all at once and the window banged to and latched itself. Now to relight the candles and see what damage, if any, had been done. No, nothing seemed amiss; no glass even was broken in the casement. But the noise had evidently roused at least one member of the household: the Colonel was to be heard stumping in his stockinged feet on the floor above, and growling.

45 *formal:* in the scene
46 *literary:* a sudden, strong wind

Quickly as it had risen, the wind did not fall at once. On it went, moaning and rushing past the house, at times rising to a cry so desolate that, as Parkins disinterestedly said, it might have made fanciful people feel quite uncomfortable; even the unimaginative, he thought after a quarter of an hour, might be happier without it.

Whether it was the wind, or the excitement of golf, or of the researches in the preceptory that kept Parkins awake, he was not sure. Awake he remained, in any case, long enough to fancy (as I am afraid I often do myself under such conditions) that he was the victim of all manner of fatal disorders: he would lie counting the beats of his heart, convinced that it was going to stop work every moment, and would entertain grave suspicions of his lungs, brain, liver, etc. – suspicions which he was sure would be dispelled by the return of daylight, but which until then refused to be put aside.

He found a little vicarious comfort in the idea that someone else was **in the same boat**. A near neighbour (in the darkness it was not easy to tell his direction) was tossing and rustling in his bed, too.

The next stage was that Parkins shut his eyes and determined to give sleep every chance. Here again over-excitement asserted itself in another form – that of making pictures. *Experto crede*[47], pictures do come to the closed eyes of one trying to sleep, and are often so little to his taste that he must open his eyes and disperse them.

Parkins's experience on this occasion was a very distressing one. He found that the picture which presented itself to him was continuous. When he opened his eyes, of course, it went; but when he shut them once more it framed itself afresh, and acted itself out again, neither quicker nor slower than before. What he saw was this:

A long stretch of shore – shingle edged by sand, and intersected at short intervals with black groynes running down to the water – a scene, in fact, so like that of his afternoon's walk that, in

47 a Latin motto which means, *Believe me*

the absence of any landmark, it could not be distinguished therefrom. The light was obscure, conveying an impression of gathering storm, late winter evening, and slight cold rain. On this bleak stage at first no actor was visible. When, in the distance, a bobbing black object appeared; a moment more, and it was a man running, jumping, clambering over the groynes, and every few seconds looking eagerly back. The nearer he came the more obvious it was that he was not only anxious, but even terribly frightened, though his face was not to be distinguished. He was, moreover, almost at the end of his strength. On he came; each successive obstacle seemed to cause him more difficulty than the last. 'Will he get over this next one?' thought Parkins; 'it seems a little higher than the others.' Yes; half climbing, half throwing himself, he did get over, and fell all in a heap on the other side (the side nearest to the spectator). There, as if really unable to get up again, he remained crouching under the groyne, looking up in an attitude of painful anxiety.

So far no cause whatever for the fear of the runner had been shown; but now there began to be seen, far up the shore, a little flicker of something light-coloured moving **to and fro** with great swiftness and irregularity. Rapidly growing larger, it, too, declared itself as a figure in pale, fluttering draperies[48], ill-defined. There was something about its motion which made Parkins very unwilling to see it at close quarters. It would stop, raise arms, bow itself toward the sand, then run stooping across the beach to the water-edge and back again; and then, rising upright, once more continue its course forward at a speed that was startling and terrifying. The moment came when the pursuer was hovering about from left to right only a few yards beyond the groyne where the runner lay in hiding. After two or three ineffectual castings hither and thither it came to a stop, stood upright, with arms raised high, and then darted straight forward towards the groyne.

It was at this point that Parkins always failed in his resolution to keep his eyes shut. With many **misgivings** as to incipient[49]

48 *old-fashioned:* hanging cloth; curtains
49 *formal:* just beginning to appear or develop

failure of eyesight, overworked brain, excessive smoking, and so on, he finally resigned himself to light his candle, get out a book, and pass the night waking, rather than be tormented by this persistent panorama, which he saw clearly enough could only be a morbid reflection of his walk and his thoughts on that very day.

The scraping of match on box and the glare of light must have startled some creatures of the night – rats or what not – which he heard scurry across the floor from the side of his bed with much rustling. Dear, dear! the match is out! Fool that it is! But the second one burnt better, and a candle and book were duly procured, **over which Parkins pored** till sleep of a wholesome kind came upon him, and that in no long space. For about the first time in his orderly and prudent life he forgot to blow out the candle, and when he was called next morning at eight there was still a flicker in the socket and a sad mess of guttered grease[50] on the top of the little table.

After breakfast he was in his room, putting the finishing touches to his golfing costume – fortune had again allotted the Colonel to him for a partner – when one of the maids came in.

'Oh, if you please,' she said, 'would you like any extra blankets on your bed, sir?'

'Ah! thank you,' said Parkins. 'Yes, I think I should like one. It seems likely to turn rather colder.'

In a very short time the maid was back with the blanket.

'Which bed should I put it on, sir?' she asked.

'What? Why, that one – the one I slept in last night,' he said, pointing to it.

'Oh yes! I beg your pardon, sir, but you seemed to have tried both of 'em; leastways, we had to make 'em both up this morning.'

'Really? How very absurd!' said Parkins. 'I certainly never touched the other, except to lay some things on it. Did it actually seem to have been slept in?'

'Oh yes, sir!' said the maid. 'Why, all the things was crumpled

50 the wax that has melted from the candle as it burnt

and throwed about all ways, if you'll excuse me, sir – quite as if anyone 'adn't passed but a very poor night, sir.'

'Dear me,' said Parkins. 'Well, I may have disordered it more than I thought when I unpacked my things. I'm very sorry to have given you the trouble, I'm sure. I expect a friend of mine soon, by the way – a gentleman from Cambridge – to come and occupy it for a night or two. That will be all right, I suppose, won't it?'

'Oh yes, to be sure, sir. Thank you, sir. It's no trouble, I'm sure,' said the maid, and departed to giggle with her colleagues.

Parkins set forth, with a stern determination to improve his game.

I am glad to be able to report that he succeeded so far in this enterprise that the Colonel, who had been rather repining[51] at the prospect of a second day's play in his company, became quite chatty as the morning advanced; and his voice boomed out over the flats, as certain also of our own minor poets have said, 'like some great bourdon[52] in a minster[53] tower.'

'Extraordinary wind, that, we had last night,' he said. 'In my old home we should have said someone had been whistling for it.'

'Should you, indeed!' said Parkins. 'Is there a superstition of that kind still current in your part of the country?'

'I don't know about superstition,' said the Colonel. 'They believe in it all over Denmark and Norway, as well as on the Yorkshire coast; and my experience is, mind you, that there's generally **something at the bottom of** what these country-folk hold to, and have held to for generations. But it's your drive' (or whatever it might have been: the golfing reader will have to imagine appropriate digressions at the proper intervals). When conversation was resumed, Parkins said with a slight hesitancy: 'Apropos of[54] what you were saying just now, Colonel, I think I ought to tell you that my own views on such subjects are very

51 *old-fashioned:* feeling unhappy about something
52 a large bell
53 a large and important church
54 *formal:* going back to

strong. I am, in fact, a convinced disbeliever in what is called the "supernatural."'

'What!' said the Colonel, 'do you mean to tell me you don't believe in second-sight, or ghosts, or anything of that kind?'

'In nothing whatever of that kind,' returned Parkins firmly.

'Well,' said the Colonel, 'but it appears to me at that rate, sir, that you must be little better than a Sadducee[55].'

Parkins was on the point of answering that, in his opinion, the Sadducees were the most sensible sons he had ever read of in the Old Testament; but, feeling some doubt as to whether much mention of them was to be found in that work, he preferred to laugh the accusation off.

'Perhaps I am,' he said; 'but – Here, give me my cleek, boy! – Excuse me one moment, Colonel.' A short interval. 'Now, as to whistling for the wind, let me give you my theory about it. The laws which govern winds are really not at all perfectly known – to fisher-folk and such, of course, not known at all. A man or woman of eccentric habits, perhaps, or a stranger, is seen repeatedly on the beach at some unusual hour, and is heard whistling. Soon afterwards a violent wind rises; a man who could read the sky perfectly or who possessed a barometer could have foretold that it would. The simple people of a fishing-village have no barometers, and only a few rough rules for prophesying weather. What more natural than that the eccentric personage I postulated[56] should be regarded as having raised the wind, or that he or she should clutch eagerly at the reputation of being able to do so? Now, take last night's wind: as it happens, I myself was whistling. I blew a whistle twice, and the wind seemed to come absolutely in answer to my call. If anyone had seen me...'

The audience had been a little restive under this harangue[57], and Parkins had, I fear, fallen somewhat into the tone of a lecturer; but at the last sentence the Colonel stopped.

55 an ancient Jewish sect which was said to refute the existence of the soul, the spirit or life after death
56 *formal, old-fashioned*: mentioned previously
57 *formal, old-fashioned*: rant; an occasion when someone angrily shouts at, or criticizes, another person

'Whistling, were you?' he said. 'And what sort of whistle did you use? Play this stroke first.' Interval.

'About that whistle you were asking, Colonel. It's rather a curious one. I have it in my – No; I see I've left it in my room. As a matter of fact, I found it yesterday.'

And then Parkins narrated the manner of his discovery of the whistle, upon hearing which the Colonel grunted, and opined[58] that, in Parkins's place, he should himself be careful about using a thing that had belonged to a set of Papists[59], of whom, speaking generally, it might be affirmed that you never knew what they might not have been up to. From this topic he diverged to the enormities of the Vicar, who had given notice on the previous Sunday that Friday would be the Feast of St. Thomas the Apostle, and that there would be service at eleven o'clock in the church. This and other similar proceedings constituted in the Colonel's view a strong presumption that the Vicar was a concealed Papist, if not a Jesuit[60]; and Parkins, who could not very readily follow the Colonel in this region, did not disagree with him. In fact, they got on so well together in the morning that there was no talk on either side of their separating after lunch.

Both continued to play well during the afternoon, or, at least, well enough to make them forget everything else until the light began to fail them. Not until then did Parkins remember that he had meant to do some more investigating at the preceptory; but it was of no great importance, he reflected. One day was as good as another; he might as well go home with the Colonel.

As they turned the corner of the house, the Colonel was almost knocked down by a boy who rushed into him at the very top of his speed, and then, instead of running away, remained hanging on to him and panting. The first words of the warrior were naturally those of reproof and objurgation[61], but he quickly discerned that the boy was almost speechless with fright.

58 *very formal:* to state your opinion
59 *offensive:* Roman Catholics, followers of the Pope
60 a priest that belongs to the Society of Jesus, founded in 1534
61 *old-fashioned, formal:* telling someone that they have behaved badly

Inquiries were useless at first. When the boy got his breath he began to howl, and still clung to the Colonel's legs. He was at last detached, but continued to howl.

'What in the world *is* the matter with you? What have you been up to? What have you seen?' said the two men.

'Ow, I seen it wive at me out of the winder,' wailed the boy, 'and I don't like it.'

'What window?' said the irritated Colonel. 'Come, **pull yourself together**, my boy.'

'The front winder it was, at the 'otel,' said the boy.

At this point Parkins was in favour of sending the boy home, but the Colonel refused; he wanted to get to the bottom of it, he said; it was most dangerous to give a boy such a fright as this one had had, and if it **turned out** that people had been playing jokes, they should suffer for it in some way. And by a series of questions he made out this story: The boy had been playing about on the grass in front of the Globe with some others; then they had gone home to their teas, and he was just going, when he happened to look up at the front winder and see it a-wiving at him. *It* seemed to be a figure of some sort, in white as far as he knew – couldn't see its face; but it wived at him, and it warn't a right thing – not to say not a right person. Was there a light in the room? No, he didn't think to look if there was a light. Which was the window? Was it the top one or the second one? The seckind one it was – the big winder what got two little uns at the sides.

'Very well, my boy,' said the Colonel, after a few more questions. 'You run away home now. I expect it was some person trying to give you a start. Another time, like a brave English boy, you just throw a stone – well, no, not that exactly, but you go and speak to the waiter, or to Mr. Simpson, the landlord, and – yes – and say that I advised you to do so.'

The boy's face expressed some of the doubt he felt as to the likelihood of Mr. Simpson's lending a favourable ear to his complaint, but the Colonel did not appear to perceive this, and went on:

'And here's a sixpence – no, I see it's a shilling – and you be off home, and don't think any more about it.'

The youth hurried off with agitated thanks, and the Colonel and Parkins went round to the front of the Globe and reconnoitred[62]. There was only one window answering to the description they had been hearing.

'Well, that's curious,' said Parkins; 'it's evidently my window the lad was talking about. Will you come up for a moment, Colonel Wilson? We ought to be able to see if anyone has been taking liberties in my room.'

They were soon in the passage, and Parkins made as if to open the door. Then he stopped and felt in his pockets.

'This is more serious than I thought,' was his next remark. 'I remember now that before I started this morning I locked the door. It is locked now, and, what is more, here is the key.' And he held it up. 'Now,' he went on, 'if the servants are in the habit of going into one's room during the day when one is away, I can only say that – well, that I don't approve of it at all.' Conscious of a somewhat weak climax, he busied himself in opening the door (which was indeed locked) and in lighting candles. 'No,' he said, 'nothing seems disturbed.'

'Except your bed,' put in the Colonel.

'Excuse me, that isn't my bed,' said Parkins. 'I don't use that one. But it does look as if someone had been playing tricks with it.'

It certainly did: the clothes were bundled up and twisted together in a most tortuous confusion. Parkins pondered.

'That must be it,' he said at last: 'I disordered the clothes last night in unpacking, and they haven't made it since. Perhaps they came in to make it, and that boy saw them through the window; and then they were called away and locked the door after them. Yes, I think that must be it.'

'Well, ring and ask,' said the Colonel, and this appealed to Parkins as practical.

The maid appeared, and, to make a long story short, deposed[63] that she had made the bed in the morning when the gentleman was in the room, and hadn't been there since. No, she hadn't no

62 *old-fashioned, formal, military:* to go and get information about an area
63 *legal:* to testify; to give information about something, usually in a court of law

other key. Mr. Simpson he kep' the keys; he'd be able to tell the gentleman if anyone had been up.

This was a puzzle. Investigation showed that nothing of value had been taken, and Parkins remembered the disposition of the small objects on tables and so forth well enough to be pretty sure that no pranks had been played with them. Mr. and Mrs. Simpson furthermore agreed that neither of them had given the duplicate key of the room to any person whatever during the day. Nor could Parkins, fair-minded man as he was, detect anything in the demeanour of master, mistress, or maid that indicated guilt. He was much more inclined to think that the boy had been imposing on the Colonel.

The latter was unwontedly[64] silent and **pensive** at dinner and throughout the evening. When he bade good night to Parkins, he murmured in a gruff undertone:

'You know where I am if you want me during the night.'

'Why, yes, thank you, Colonel Wilson, I think I do; but there isn't much prospect of my disturbing you, I hope. By the way,' he added, 'did I show you that old whistle I spoke of? I think not. Well, here it is.'

The Colonel turned it over gingerly in the light of the candle.

'Can you make anything of the inscription?' asked Parkins, as he took it back.

'No, not in this light. What do you mean to do with it?'

'Oh, well, when I get back to Cambridge I shall submit it to some of the archaeologists there, and see what they think of it; and very likely, if they consider it worth having, I may present it to one of the museums.'

'M!' said the Colonel. 'Well, you may be right. All I know is that, if it were mine, I should chuck it straight into the sea. It's no use talking, I'm well aware, but I expect that with you it's a case of live and learn. I hope so, I'm sure, and I wish you a good night.'

He turned away, leaving Parkins in act to speak[65] at the

64 *formal:* unusually
65 *old-fashioned, phrase 'in act to speak':* about to speak

bottom of the stair, and soon each was in his own bedroom.

By some unfortunate accident, there were neither blinds nor curtains to the windows of the Professor's room. The previous night he had thought little of this, but to-night there seemed every prospect of a bright moon rising to shine directly on his bed, and probably wake him later on. When he noticed this he was a good deal annoyed, but, with an ingenuity which I can only envy, he succeeded in **rigging up**, with the help of a railway-rug, some safety-pins, and a stick and umbrella, a screen which, if it only held together, would completely keep the moonlight off his bed. And shortly afterwards he was comfortably in that bed. When he had read a somewhat solid work long enough to produce a decided wish for sleep, he cast a drowsy glance round the room, blew out the candle, and fell back upon the pillow.

He must have slept soundly for an hour or more, when a sudden clatter shook him up in a most unwelcome manner. In a moment he realised what had happened: his carefully-constructed screen had given way, and a very bright frosty moon was shining directly on his face. This was highly annoying. Could he possibly get up and reconstruct the screen? or could he manage to sleep if he did not?

For some minutes he lay and pondered over the possibilities; then he turned over sharply, and with all his eyes open lay breathlessly listening. There had been a movement, he was sure, in the empty bed on the opposite side of the room. To-morrow he would have it moved, for there must be rats or something playing about in it. It was quiet now. No! the **commotion** began again. There was a rustling and shaking: surely more than any rat could cause.

I can figure to myself something of the Professor's bewilderment and horror, for I have in a dream thirty years back seen the same thing happen; but the reader will hardly, perhaps, imagine how dreadful it was to him to see a figure suddenly sit up in what he had known was an empty bed. He was out of his own bed in one bound, and made a dash towards the window, where lay his only weapon, the stick with which he had propped his screen. This was, as it turned out, the worst thing he could have done, because the personage in the empty bed, with a sudden motion, slipped from the bed and took up a position, with outspread arms, between the two beds, and in front of the door. Parkins watched it in a horrid perplexity. Somehow, the idea of getting past it and escaping through the door was intolerable to him; he could not have borne – he didn't know why – to touch it; and as for its touching him, he would sooner dash himself through the window than have that happen. It stood for the moment in a band of dark shadow, and he had not seen what its face was like. Now it began to move, in a stooping posture, and all at once the spectator realised, with some horror and some relief, that it must be blind, for it seemed to feel about it with its muffled arms in a groping and random fashion. Turning half away from him, it became suddenly conscious of the bed he had just left, and darted towards it, and bent over and felt the pillows in a way which made Parkins shudder as he had never in his life thought it possible. In a very few moments it seemed to know that the bed was empty, and then, moving forward into the area of light and facing the window, it showed for the first time what manner of thing it was.

Parkins, who very much dislikes being questioned about it, did once describe something of it in my hearing, and I gathered that what he chiefly remembers about it is a horrible, an intensely horrible, face *of crumpled linen*. What expression he read upon it he could not or would not tell, but that the fear of it went nigh[66] to maddening him is certain.

But he was not at leisure to watch it for long. With formidable quickness it moved into the middle of the room, and, as it groped and waved, one corner of its draperies swept across Parkins's face. He could not – though he knew how perilous a sound was – he could not keep back a cry of disgust, and this gave the searcher an instant clue. It leapt towards him upon the instant, and the next moment he was half-way through the window backwards,

66 *old-fashioned:* near

uttering cry upon cry at the utmost pitch of his voice, and the linen face was thrust close into his own. At this, almost the last possible second, deliverance came, as you will have guessed: the Colonel burst the door open, and was just in time to see the dreadful group at the window. When he reached the figures only one was left. Parkins sank forward into the room in a faint, and before him on the floor lay a tumbled heap of bed-clothes.

Colonel Wilson asked no questions, but busied himself in keeping everyone else out of the room and in getting Parkins back to his bed; and himself, wrapped in a rug, occupied the other bed for the rest of the night. Early on the next day Rogers arrived, more welcome than he would have been a day before, and the three of them held a very long consultation in the Professor's room. At the end of it the Colonel left the hotel door carrying a small object between his finger and thumb, which he cast as far into the sea as a very brawny[67] arm could send it. Later on the smoke of a burning ascended from the back premises of the Globe.

Exactly what explanation was patched up for the staff and visitors at the hotel I must confess I do not recollect. The Professor was somehow cleared of the ready suspicion of delirium tremens[68], and the hotel of the reputation of a troubled house.

There is not much question as to what would have happened to Parkins if the Colonel had not intervened when he did. He would either have fallen out of the window or else lost his wits. But it is not so evident what more the creature that came in answer to the whistle could have done than frighten. There seemed to be absolutely nothing material about it save the bed-clothes of which it had made itself a body. The Colonel, who remembered a not very dissimilar occurrence in India, was of opinion that if Parkins had closed with it[69] it could really have done very little, and that its one power was that of frightening. The whole thing, he said, served to confirm his opinion of the Church of Rome.

67 *old-fashioned:* muscular, physically strong
68 *medical:* a serious medical condition caused by drinking to much
69 *old-fashioned, phrase 'closed with it': fought,* from verb *to fight*

There is really nothing more to tell, but, as you may imagine, the Professor's views on certain points are less **clear cut** than they used to be. His nerves, too, have suffered: he cannot even now see a surplice[70] hanging on a door quite unmoved, and the spectacle of a scarecrow in a field late on a winter afternoon has cost him more than one sleepless night.

70 a loose white piece of clothing, worn over other clothes by priests

Post-reading exercises

Understanding the story

1 **Use these questions to help you check that you have understood the story.**

Before leaving for Burnstow...

1 Where does the opening conversation take place?
2 What do you learn about the main character, Professor Parkins and his beliefs and attitudes?
3 How is he going to spend his holiday?

In Burnstow...

4 What did Parkins do as soon as he arrived?
5 What does this tell you about his character?
6 Why did he choose to walk home alone at the end of the first day?
7 What was he looking for? What did he find?
8 Who, or what, did he see on the beach as he walked home?
9 What did it make him think of?
10 Who reminded him of the metal object he'd found that day?
11 What did he see through the window as he cleaned the whistle?
12 What happened when he blew on it?
13 Why couldn't he get to sleep that night?
14 What sounds did he hear in his room when he was trying to light the candle?
15 What had happened to the second bed? Why was it *disordered*?
16 Why did the Colonel and Parkins start talking about winds and whistles?
17 What was Parkins's reaction to the Colonel's *superstitions*?
18 What was the Colonel's reaction to Parkins's story about the whistle?
19 What had the boy seen and where had he seen it?
20 What puzzled the two men about the figure seen at the window?
21 Why was the colonel so quiet that evening? What was worrying him?
22 Why did Parkins put up a screen in his room?
23 How did Parkins first become aware of the presence in his room?
24 How did he react?
25 What was his mistake?
26 Why did the figure terrify him?
27 What would have happened if the Colonel hadn't arrived?

28 What did the Colonel do with the whistle? Why?
29 What did they burn at the back of the hotel?
30 How did the experience affect the Professor?

Language study

As in all James's stories, the author creates a contrast between the ordinary, sometimes tedious details of the academic's life, and the mysterious setting of the story and the extraordinary events of the main character's experience of the supernatural. One of the linguistic devices James uses to emphasise this contrast is **fronting**.

Fronting

Form

The standard, basic word order of sentences in English is subject+verb+ object. When we change the order of these – and, for example, start a sentence with the verb or the object – it is called 'fronting'. Notice the position of the subject in the sentences below. The words in **bold italic** are the subjects of the sentence.

> (a) This **he** accomplished, I may say, in the most literal sense.
>
> (b) Bleak and solemn was **the view**.
>
> (c) On **he** came; each successive obstacle seemed to cause him more difficulty than the last.

1 **Compare the sentences above with the more common subject+verb+object word order in the sentences below.**

He accomplished this, I may say, in the most literal sense.
The view was bleak and solemn.
He came on; each successive obstacle seemed to cause him more difficulty than the last.

Use

Fronting is often used in literary writing and poetry, to create a dramatic, or comic, effect. It can help to focus attention on a particular event or description.

Look again at the first example above, sentence (a). The fronted object (first word of the sentence) is This – the word refers to something in the previous paragraph where Parkins's thoughts are reported:

> '*I might walk home to-night along the beach,*' *he reflected* – '*yes, and take a look* – *there will be light enough for that* – *at the ruins of which Disney was talking. I don't exactly know where they are, by the way; but I expect I can hardly help* **stumbling on them.**'

The Professor is using *stumble on* to mean *to find accidentally*. The author plays with the double meaning of the verb, which also means 'to fall'. The fronting is used to emphasise the literary and comic effect as the Professor does, literally *stumble* (fall) on the ruins. The fronting achieves two effects:

1 to encourage the reader to gently laugh at the main character
2 to focus attention on the first significant event in the story – the discovery of the ruins.

2 Look again at the other two sentences, (b) and (c), and answer the following questions.

1 What part of the sentence is being fronted?
2 What is being emphasised, an event or a description?
3 What effect is being created?

3 Rewrite these sentences using standard word order.

1 *His foot caught … and over he went.* [page 61]

2 *And now followed another little discovery.* [page 61]

3 *On it went, moaning and rushing past the house.* [page 66]

4 *Awake he remained.* [page 66]

5 *What expression he read upon it he could not or would not tell.* [page 76]

6 *Exactly what explanation was patched up for the staff and visitors at the hotel I must confess I do not recollect.* [page 77]

4 Look at the sentences above in the context of the story. What event or description is being emphasised in each case?

Understatement and circumlocation

Professor Parkins is a slightly pompous, self-important academic. This is shown in the way he speaks and thinks. He often speaks indirectly and uses too many words. The narrative reflects his character – it uses over-complicated, wordy sentences to describe what is happening to him, and what he is thinking.

Look at this example:

The object which he now had safe in this pocket was bound to be of some slight value at least, he felt sure.

Parkins is really saying that he thinks the object is worth keeping, but he does not say this in a simple, direct manner. The narrative – reporting Parkins's thoughts – uses the words *some slight* and *at least* when he is thinking about the value of the object – this means that it is not important, and has a low value to Parkins. He is trying not to feel excitement about the discovery by using **understatement**.

5 **Look at these extracts. Underline the phrases or expressions that show understatement and rewrite them in simple, clear English.**

1 In response to Rogers's suggestion that he might visit Parkins on his holiday, an idea that Parkins does not like at all.

I was considering whether ... (mind, I shouldn't have said this if you hadn't pressed me) you would not constitute something in the nature of a hindrance to my work. [page 58]

2 Talking about an evening spent with the Colonel:

He felt that he had spent his evening in quite a satisfactory way, and that, even for so long as a fortnight or three weeks, life at the Globe would be supportable under similar conditions. [page 63]

3 Talking about the wind whistling outside his window at night:

It might have made fanciful people feel quite uncomfortable; even the unimaginative, he thought after a quarter of an hour, might be happier without it. [page 66]

Literary analysis

Plot

1 List the main events in the story. Notice how they build up to the final scene. Notice how the details of ordinary, day-to-day life gradually get pushed to one side as the ghost's presence grows.

2 The ghost makes a fairly early appearance in the story. When does Parkins first see it? What other signs are given for its presence? How does Parkins feel about these signs? In what other ways is the ghost's presence felt?

3 What effect did the experience have on Parkins? In what way did it change his attitude to ghosts?

Character

4 Who are the three main characters in the story? What do we know about them? Choose two or three adjectives to describe each character.

5 Think of the character of Parkins. To what extent is he a stereotype of a dry, boring academic? Why is it important that he is so sure that ghosts do not exist?

6 In what ways are Parkins and Colonel Wilson similar? In what ways are they different? Think about their personalities, their background and their attitudes to ghosts and the supernatural.

Narration

7 The story is told by a third-person narrator, a storyteller, who often speaks directly to the reader. Look at the first section (before Parkins arrives in Burnstow), and find three examples of the author speaking directly to the reader. What effect does this style create? What picture do we get of the character of the narrator?

8 What is the purpose of the first section of the story? Why is this important?

9 The narrator mainly tells the story from the point of view of the main character, Parkins. How does Parkins's interpretation of events affect the telling of the story? How would the story have been different if it had been told from the Colonel's point of view?

Atmosphere

10 Think about what the following elements of the story add to its general atmosphere: the setting, the weather, the history of the site.

11 Think about how the writer builds up the picture of the ghost. What sounds, movements and colours are associated with the ghost? Why is Parkins so frightened by it? What makes it so terrifying? Are these details on the page, or in our heads?

Style

12 Look at the description of the beach as Parkins walks home on the evening he finds the whistle. Notice how the writer sets the scene for the first appearance of the ghost.

Bleak and solemn was the view on which he took a last look before starting homeward. A faint yellow light in the west showed the links, on which a few figures moving towards the club-house were still visible, the squat martello tower, the lights of Aldsey village, the pale ribbon of sands intersected at intervals by black wooden groynes, the dim and murmuring sea. The wind was bitter from the north, but was at his back when he set out for the Globe.

   – What colours are used in the description?
   – What is the visual effect of the description? How does it make you feel, as the reader?
   – What other adjectives are used?
   – What is the overall atmosphere of the scene?

13 Notice the similarities in the description of the image that comes to Parkins's mind when he blows the whistle. Look at the words in bold. What details do these refer back to in the first description?

*It was a sound, too, that seemed to have the power (which many scents possess) of forming pictures in the brain. He saw quite clearly for a moment a vision of **a wide, dark expanse** at night, with **a fresh wind blowing**, and in the midst **a lonely figure**.*

14 The ghost is first described in the images that appear in Parkins's mind as he tries to go to sleep on the second night at The Globe.

Read the passage and notice how light, speed and movement are described and how they add to the description. Look in particular at the last sentence, and underline all the verbs in the sentence. What effect is created by the list of verbs?

> ...but now there began to be seen, far up the shore, a little flicker of something light-coloured moving to and fro with great swiftness and irregularity. Rapidly growing larger, it, too, declared itself as a figure in pale, fluttering draperies, ill-defined. There was something about its motion which made Parkins very unwilling to see it at close quarters. It would stop, raise arms, bow itself toward the sand, then run stooping across the beach to the water-edge and back again; and then, rising upright, once more continue its course forward at a speed that was startling and terrifying.

15   What details from this description are repeated later, when the boy sees the ghost at the window, and when Parkins finally sees it in his bedroom? Think about how these details help build up both the image of the ghost and the suspense in the story.

Guidance to the above literary terms, answer keys to all the exercises and activities, plus a wealth of other reading-practice material, can be found on the student's section of the Macmillan Readers website at: www.macmillanenglish.com/readers.

The Monkey's Paw

by W W Jacobs

About the author

William Wymark Jacobs was a British writer of short stories and novels. He is best known for his horror story, *The Monkey's Paw*, but most of his stories were humorous, not horrific. They described the life of sailors and dockworkers in and around the London docks, where his father worked for many years.

Jacobs was born in London in 1863. He studied at Birkbeck College, which is now a part of the University of London, and in 1879 he started work in the Post Office. In 1885, he published his first short story and slowly began to make money from writing. In 1896, Jacobs published his first collection of short stories, *Many Cargoes*. By 1899, he was earning enough money from his writing to leave his job.

In the last few decades of his life he wrote very few stories, preferring instead to write adaptations of his stories for the theatre. He died in 1943 at the age of 79.

During his lifetime he was very successful, but after his death his work was soon forgotten, apart from his most successful story, *The Monkey's Paw*.

About the story

The story was first published in *Harper's Monthly Magazine* in 1902 and was also included in Jacobs' third short-story collection, *The Lady of the Barge*, which was published in the same year. It is generally considered to be a classic of horror fiction and it has appeared in several anthologies and collections. It has also been adapted for use in schools, especially in the USA, as well as for theatre, TV and radio. A number of films have been made based on the story, or taking a similar theme. The most recent was a Nepali production, *Kagbeni*, which was released in 2008. There are even home video versions available on YouTube.com.

The story is set in a house in the country at the beginning of the 20th century.

Background information

Three wishes

Most cultures have some belief or superstition built around making a wish. It may be that if you make a wish when you blow out your birthday candles, or when you see a shooting star, it will come true. One of the earliest examples of wishes in literature is that of Aladdin and the genie in the lamp in *The Book of One Thousand and One Nights*. In that story, Aladdin could make an unlimited number of wishes. In other stories, the number of wishes is restricted. The number three has become associated with wishes, and many folk tales tell of fairies or other supernatural figures who can grant three wishes. Sometimes, wording is very important – the wish may not be granted if the person making the wish has not been careful in the words they use. In other versions of wish stories, the wish comes true, but there are consequences – your wish may be granted, but it will come at a terrible price, which is what happens in *The Monkey's Paw*. In these cases, the wishes are being granted to teach a moral lesson or in order to punish greed.

Summary

It may help you to know something about what happens in the story before you read it. Don't worry, this summary does not tell you how the story ends!

One night Mr and Mrs White and their son Herbert are at home when they receive a visitor. It is an old friend of the family who has recently returned from India. He tells them the story of a monkey's paw that he is carrying with him in his pocket. Apparently, the paw is magic. A holy man has put a **spell** on it so that it can grant three wishes to three separate men.

The visitor has had his three wishes granted, as has another man before him. There are three wishes remaining. The visitor does not want to talk about his wishes; instead, he throws the monkey's paw on the fire. But Mr White saves it from the fire and asks his visitor to give it to him. His visitor explains how to make the wishes, but warns the family that it may be dangerous and tries to persuade Mr White to throw it back on the fire.

After the visitor has gone, the family joke about the paw and the wishes they can make. In the end they decide on a very modest wish, and the father asks the paw for £200. None of the family really believes the wish will come true.

The next day a stranger comes to the house – he has news for the family, and a cheque for £200. Their first wish has been granted, but at what price? Will they be able to use the other two wishes to repair the damage?

Pre-reading exercises

Key vocabulary

This section will help you familiarise yourself with some of the more specific vocabulary used in the story. You may want to use it to help you before you start reading, or as a revision exercise after you've finished the story.

Verbs of movement

The description of movement is often very important in the telling of the story – the way the characters move often tells us a lot about their state of mind.

1 Look at the list of verbs of movement below. The definitions explain the meaning of the verbs, as they are used in the story. Replace the phrases in bold in the extracts below with verbs from the list.

---

bow to bend your head forward slightly, especially to pay respect
dart to make a sudden, quick movement
fumble to try to hold, move or find something using your hands in a way that is not skilful or graceful
grope to try to get to a place by feeling with your hands
scurry to move fast with small, quick steps, like a small animal
stoop to bend the top half of your body downwards
struggle to use your strength to fight against someone or something
stumble to fall or almost fall when walking or running

---

1 *'To look at,' said the sergeant-major,* **trying to get hold of** *something in his pocket, 'it's just an ordinary little paw.'*
2 *He started up in alarm. 'Where? Where is it? What's the matter?'*
   She came **walking uncertainly** *across the room toward him.*
3 *He* **suddenly ran** *round the table.*

4 *White, with a slight cry, **crouched** down and snatched it off* [the fire].
5 *He felt his way round the table, and **felt his way** along the wall.*
6 *A stair creaked, and a squeaky mouse **ran** noisily through the wall.*
7 *The visitor **moved his head** in assent.*
8 *'It's my boy; it's Herbert!' she cried, **trying to get herself free of Mr White's** arms.*

In which extract/s is the verb
(a) replacing a long phrase?
(b) being used to avoid repetition?

Verbs to describe holding or handling an object

The story revolves around an object – the monkey's paw, and contains a number of verbs that describe how the characters hold or handle the paw.

2 Match the definitions in the box below, to the words in bold in the extracts.

1	To hold something so that it hangs or swings without touching anything
2	To take and hold something or somebody very tightly
3	To throw something using a lot of force
4	To pull or take something away very quickly, to grab

1 *He took the paw, and **dangling** it between his front finger and thumb, suddenly threw it upon the fire. White, with a slight cry, stooped down and **snatched** it off.*
2 *'I threw it on the fire. If you keep it, don't blame me for what happens. **Pitch** it on the fire again, like a sensible man.'*
3 *His hand **grasped** the monkey's paw, and with a little shiver he wiped his hand on his coat and went up to bed.*

3 Use the verbs in bold, above, to complete these sentences.

1 He picked up the ball and .... it over the wall as far and as high as he could.
2 He was so surprised he .... my arm and wouldn't let go!
3 Her brother .... the toy from her hand and ran away, laughing.
4 A single light bulb .... from the ceiling.

Main themes

Before you read the story, you may want to think about some of its main themes. The questions will help you think about the story as you're reading it for the first time. There is more discussion of the main themes in the *Literary analysis* section after the story.

Fate

One of the main themes the story explores is that of fate, or destiny. The story asks us to consider whether our futures have already been decided, or if we can change them. It also explores the idea of 'tempting fate' – the idea that trying to change our future may be dangerous, the idea that our futures have been decided by higher powers, and that we should not try to take these powers into our own hands.

4 As you read the story, think about this question:

What message is the story giving us about fate and the dangers of trying to change our destinies?

Supersition versus scepticism

The story also explores the argument between superstition and scepticism. The characters in the story joke about the magical powers of the paw, but at the same time they are also fascinated by the possibility of it being true. They claim not to believe in magic, yet they still decide to take the paw and test its powers.

5 As you read, think about these questions:

a) Why doesn't Mr White listen to the sergeant major's advice?
b) If the sergeant major knows about the dangers of using the paw, why does he give it to Mr White?
c) Why do the family make the first wish if they do not believe in the magic?

The Monkey's Paw

by W W Jacobs

I

Without[1], the night was cold and wet, but in the small parlour[2] of Laburnam Villa the blinds were drawn and the fire burned brightly. Father and son were at chess[3], the former, who possessed ideas about the game involving radical changes, putting his king into such sharp and unnecessary perils that it even provoked comment from the white-haired old lady knitting placidly by the fire.

'Hark[4] at the wind,' said Mr. White, who, having seen a fatal mistake after it was too late, was amiably desirous[5] of preventing his son from seeing it.

'I'm listening,' said the latter, grimly surveying the board as he stretched out his hand. 'Check.'

'I should hardly think that he'd come to-night,' said his father, with his hand poised over the board.

'Mate,' replied the son.

'That's the worst of living so far out,' bawled Mr. White, with sudden and unlooked-for violence; 'of all the beastly, slushy, out-of-the-way places to live in, this is the worst. Pathway's a bog[6], and the road's a **torrent**. I don't know what people are thinking about. I suppose because only two houses on the road are let, they think it doesn't matter.'

'Never mind, dear,' said his wife soothingly; 'perhaps you'll win the next one.'

Mr. White looked up sharply, just in time to intercept a

1 *old-fashioned:* outside
2 *old-fashioned:* living room
3 *old-fashioned:* 'to be at' + verb means to be busy doing something, here *playing*
4 *old-fashioned:* listen
5 *formal:* wanting to have or do something
6 an area of ground that is always very wet and soft

knowing glance between mother and son. The words died away on his lips, and he hid a guilty grin[7] in his thin grey beard.

'There he is,' said Herbert White, as the gate banged to loudly and heavy footsteps came toward the door.

The old man rose with hospitable **haste**, and opening the door, was heard condoling[8] with the new arrival. The new arrival also condoled with himself, so that Mrs. White said, 'Tut, tut!' and coughed gently as her husband entered the room, followed by a tall burly man, beady[9] of eye and rubicund[10] of visage.

'Sergeant-Major Morris,' he said, introducing him.

The sergeant-major shook hands, and taking the proffered[11] seat by the fire, watched contentedly while his host got out whisky and tumblers[12] and stood a small copper kettle on the fire.

At the third glass his eyes got brighter, and he began to talk, the little family circle regarding with eager interest this visitor from distant parts, as he squared his broad shoulders in the chair and spoke of strange scenes and doughty[13] deeds; of wars and plagues and strange peoples.

'Twenty-one years of it,' said Mr. White, nodding at his wife and son. 'When he went away he was a slip of a youth in the warehouse. Now look at him.'

'He don't look to have taken much harm,' said Mrs. White, politely.

'I'd like to go to India myself,' said the old man, 'just to look round a bit, you know.'

'Better where you are,' said the sergeant-major, shaking his head. He put down the empty glass, and sighing softly, shook it again.

'I should like to see those old temples and fakirs[14] and jugglers,'

---

7 *noun phrase:* a smile that shows that you know you are guilty of something
8 expressing sympathy
9 *literary:* small and round, like beads
10 *literary:* having a red face
11 *formal:* from *proffer* – to offer something to someone by moving it towards them
12 a drinking glass without a handle or stem
13 *old-fashioned:* determined and courageous
14 a Hindu or Muslim holy man who lives by begging

said the old man. 'What was that you started telling me the other day about a monkey's paw or something, Morris?'

'Nothing,' said the soldier hastily. 'Leastways, nothing worth hearing.'

'Monkey's paw?' said Mrs. White curiously.

'Well, it's just a bit of what you might call magic, perhaps,' said the sergeant-major off-handedly.

His three listeners leaned forward eagerly. The visitor absentmindedly put his empty glass to his lips and then set it down again. His host filled it for him.

'To look at,' said the sergeant-major, fumbling in his pocket, 'it's just an ordinary little paw, dried to a mummy.'

He took something out of his pocket and proffered it. Mrs. White drew back with a grimace, but her son, taking it, examined it curiously.

'And what is there special about it?' inquired Mr. White, as he took it from his son and, having examined it, placed it upon[15] the table.

'It had a **spell** put on it by an old fakir,' said the sergeant-major, 'a very holy man. He wanted to show that fate ruled people's lives, and that those who interfered with it did so to their sorrow. He put a spell on it so that three separate men could each have three wishes from it.'

His manner was so impressive that his hearers were conscious that their light laughter **jarred** somewhat.

'Well, why don't you have three, sir?' said Herbert White cleverly.

The soldier regarded him in the way that middle age is wont to[16] regard presumptuous youth. 'I have,' he said quietly, and his blotchy face whitened.

'And did you really have the three wishes granted?' asked Mrs. White.

'I did,' said the sergeant-major, and his glass tapped against his strong teeth.

'And has anybody else wished?' inquired the old lady.

15 *old-fashioned:* on
16 *literary, phrase 'wont to':* to have a habit of doing something

'The first man had his three wishes, yes,' was the reply. 'I don't know what the first two were, but the third was for death. That's how I got the paw.'

His tones were so grave that a **hush** fell upon the group.

'If you've had your three wishes, it's no good to you now, then, Morris,' said the old man at last. 'What do you keep it for?'

The soldier shook his head. 'Fancy, I suppose,' he said slowly.

'If you could have another three wishes,' said the old man, eyeing him keenly, 'would you have them?'

'I don't know,' said the other. 'I don't know.'

He took the paw, and dangling it between his front finger and thumb, suddenly threw it upon the fire. White, with a slight cry, stooped down and snatched it off.

'Better let it burn,' said the soldier solemnly.

'If you don't want it, Morris,' said the old man, 'give it to me.'

'I won't,' said his friend doggedly. 'I threw it on the fire. If you keep it, don't blame me for what happens. Pitch it on the fire again, like a sensible man.'

The other shook his head and examined his new possession closely. 'How do you do it?' he inquired.

'Hold it up in your right hand and wish aloud,' said the sergeant-major, 'but I warn you of the consequences.'

'Sounds like the Arabian Nights[17],' said Mrs White, as she rose and began to set the supper. 'Don't you think you might wish for four pairs of hands for me?'

Her husband drew the talisman[18] from his pocket and then all three burst into laughter as the sergeant-major, with a look of alarm on his face, caught him by the arm.

'If you must wish,' he said gruffly, 'wish for something sensible.'

Mr. White dropped it back into his pocket, and placing chairs, motioned his friend to the table. In the business of supper

17 the English version of a collection of ancient Persian and Arabic tales, including the tale of Aladdin's lamp
18 *mostly literary:* an object that someone believes has special powers, especially the power to protect them from bad things

the talisman was partly forgotten, and afterward the three sat listening in an **enthralled** fashion to a second instalment of the soldier's adventures in India.

'If the tale about the monkey paw is not more truthful than those he has been telling us,' said Herbert, as the door closed behind their guest, just in time for him to catch the last train, 'we shan't make much out of it.'

'Did you give him anything for it, father?' inquired Mrs. White, regarding her husband closely.

'A trifle,' said he, colouring slightly. 'He didn't want it, but I made him take it. And he pressed me again to throw it away.'

'Likely,' said Herbert, with pretended horror. 'Why, we're going to be rich, and famous, and happy. Wish to be an emperor, father, to begin with; then you can't be henpecked.[19]'

He darted round the table, pursued by the maligned Mrs. White armed with an antimacassar[20].

Mr. White took the paw from his pocket and eyed it **dubiously**. 'I don't know what to wish for, and that's a fact,' he said slowly. 'It seems to me I've got all I want.'

'If you only cleared the house[21], you'd be quite happy, wouldn't you?' said Herbert, with his hand on his shoulder. 'Well, wish for two hundred pounds, then; that'll just do it.'

His father, smiling shamefacedly at his own credulity, held up the talisman, as his son, with a solemn face somewhat **marred** by a wink at his mother, sat down at the piano and struck a few impressive chords.

'I wish for two hundred pounds,' said the old man distinctly.

A fine crash from the piano greeted the words, interrupted by a shuddering cry from the old man. His wife and son ran toward him.

'It moved,' he cried, with a glance of disgust at the object as it lay on the floor. 'As I wished it twisted in my hands like a snake.'

19 criticised and given orders all the time by a wife or female partner
20 *old-fashioned:* a piece of cloth that was placed on the back of chairs or sofas to protect the material from hair grease
21 made the last mortgage payment to the bank

'Well, I don't see the money,' said his son, as he picked it up and placed it on the table, 'and I bet I never shall.'

'It must have been your fancy, father,' said his wife, regarding him anxiously.

He shook his head. 'Never mind, though; there's no harm done, but it gave me a shock all the same.'

They sat down by the fire again while the two men finished their pipes. Outside, the wind was higher than ever, and the old man started nervously at the sound of a door banging upstairs. A silence unusual and depressing settled upon all three, which lasted until the old couple rose to retire for the night.

'I expect you'll find the cash tied up in a big bag in the middle of your bed,' said Herbert, as he bade them good-night, 'and something horrible squatting up on top of the wardrobe watching you as you pocket your ill-gotten gains[22].'

He sat alone in the darkness, gazing at the dying fire, and seeing faces in it. The last face was so horrible and so simian[23] that he gazed at it in amazement. It got so vivid that, with a little uneasy laugh, he felt on the table for a glass containing a little water to throw over it. His hand grasped the monkey's paw, and with a little shiver he wiped his hand on his coat and went up to bed.

II

In the brightness of the wintry sun next morning as it streamed over the breakfast table Herbert laughed at his fears. There was an air of prosaic wholesomeness about the room which it had lacked on the previous night, and the dirty, shrivelled little paw was pitched on the sideboard with a carelessness which betokened[24] no great belief in its virtues.

'I suppose all old soldiers are the same,' said Mrs White. 'The idea of our listening to such nonsense! How could wishes be granted in these days? And if they could, how could two hundred pounds hurt you, father?'

22 *often humorous:* money or property that someone has gained in an illegal or dishonest way
23 *formal:* similar to, or connected to, a monkey or an ape
24 *literary:* to show, to be a sign of something

'Might drop on his head from the sky,' said the frivolous Herbert.

'Morris said the things happened so naturally,' said his father, 'that you might if you so wished attribute it to coincidence.'

'Well, don't break into the money before I come back,' said Herbert, as he rose from the table. 'I'm afraid it'll turn you into a mean, **avaricious** man, and we shall have to disown you.'

His mother laughed, and following him to the door, watched him down the road, and returning to the breakfast table, was very happy **at the expense of** her husband's credulity. All of which did not prevent her from scurrying to the door at the postman's knock, nor prevent her from referring somewhat shortly to retired sergeant-majors of bibulous[25] habits when she found that the post brought a tailor's bill.

'Herbert will have some more of his funny remarks, I expect, when he comes home,' she said, as they sat at dinner.

'I dare say,' said Mr. White, pouring himself out some beer; 'but for all that, the thing moved in my hand; that I'll swear to.'

'You thought it did,' said the old lady soothingly.

'I say it did,' replied the other. 'There was no thought about it; I had just— What's the matter?'

His wife made no reply. She was watching the mysterious movements of a man outside, who, peering in an undecided fashion at the house, appeared to be trying to make up his mind to enter. In mental connection with the two hundred pounds, she noticed that the stranger was well dressed and wore a silk hat of glossy newness. Three times he paused at the gate, and then walked on again. The fourth time he stood with his hand upon it, and then with sudden resolution flung it open and walked up the path. Mrs. White at the same moment placed her hands behind her, and hurriedly unfastening the strings of her apron, put that useful article of apparel[26] beneath the cushion of her chair.

25 *humorous:* who enjoys drinking alcohol
26 *formal:* piece of clothing

She brought the stranger, who seemed ill at ease, into the room. He gazed at her furtively, and listened in a preoccupied fashion as the old lady apologized for the appearance of the room, and her husband's coat, a garment which he usually reserved for the garden. She then waited as patiently as her sex[27] would permit, for him to broach his business, but he was at first strangely silent.

'I – was asked to call,' he said at last, and stooped and picked a piece of cotton from his trousers. 'I come from Maw and Meggins.'

The old lady started. 'Is anything the matter?' she asked breathlessly. 'Has anything happened to Herbert? What is it? What is it?'

Her husband interposed. 'There, there, mother,' he said hastily. 'Sit down, and don't **jump to conclusions**. You've not brought bad news, I'm sure, sir' and he eyed the other wistfully.

'I'm sorry— ' began the visitor.

'Is he hurt?' demanded the mother.

The visitor bowed in assent. 'Badly hurt,' he said quietly, 'but he is not in any pain.'

'Oh, thank God!' said the old woman, clasping her hands. 'Thank God for that! Thank— '

She broke off suddenly as the sinister meaning of the assurance dawned upon her and she saw the awful confirmation of her fears in the other's averted face. She caught her breath, and turning to her slower-witted husband, laid her trembling old hand upon his. There was a long silence.

'He was caught in the machinery,' said the visitor at length, in a low voice.

'Caught in the machinery,' repeated Mr. White, in a dazed fashion, 'yes.'

He sat staring blankly out at the window, and taking his wife's hand between his own, pressed it as he had been wont to do in their old courting days nearly forty years before.

'He was the only one left to us,' he said, turning gently to the visitor. 'It is hard.'

27 *literary:* gender, ie being a woman; here it is offensive, as the text implies that she is not very patient because women cannot be very patient

The other coughed, and rising, walked slowly to the window. 'The firm wished me to convey their sincere sympathy with you in your great loss,' he said, without looking round. 'I beg that you will understand I am only their servant and merely obeying orders.'

There was no reply; the old woman's face was white, her eyes staring, and her breath inaudible; on the husband's face was a look such as his friend the sergeant might have carried into his first action.

'I was to say that Maw and Meggins disclaim all responsibility,' continued the other. 'They admit no liability at all, but in consideration of your son's services they wish to present you with a certain sum as compensation.'

Mr. White dropped his wife's hand, and rising to his feet, gazed with a look of horror at his visitor. His dry lips shaped the words, 'How much?'

'Two hundred pounds,' was the answer.

Unconscious of his wife's shriek, the old man smiled faintly, put out his hands like a sightless man, and dropped, a senseless heap, to the floor.

III

In the huge new cemetery, some two miles distant, the old people buried their dead, and came back to a house steeped in shadow and silence. It was all over so quickly that at first they could hardly realize it, and remained in a state of expectation as though of something else to happen – something else which was to lighten this load, too heavy for old hearts to bear.

But the days passed, and expectation gave place to resignation – the hopeless resignation of the old, sometimes miscalled, apathy. Sometimes they hardly exchanged a word, for now they had nothing to talk about, and their days were long with weariness.

It was about a week after that that the old man, waking suddenly in the night, stretched out his hand and found himself alone.

The room was in darkness, and the sound of subdued **weeping** came from the window. He raised himself in bed and listened.

'Come back,' he said tenderly. 'You will be cold.'

'It is colder for my son,' said the old woman, and wept afresh.

The sound of her sobs died away on his ears. The bed was warm, and his eyes heavy with sleep. He dozed fitfully, and then slept until a sudden wild cry from his wife awoke him with a start.

'The paw!' she cried wildly. 'The monkey's paw!'

He started up in alarm. 'Where? Where is it? What's the matter?'

She came stumbling across the room toward him. 'I want it,' she said quietly. 'You've not destroyed it?'

'It's in the parlour, on the bracket,' he replied, marvelling. 'Why?'

She cried and laughed together, and bending over, kissed his cheek.

'I only just thought of it,' she said hysterically. 'Why didn't I think of it before? Why didn't you think of it?'

'Think of what?' he questioned.

'The other two wishes,' she replied rapidly. 'We've only had one.'

'Was not that enough?' he demanded fiercely.

'No,' she cried, triumphantly; 'we'll have one more. Go down and get it quickly, and wish our boy alive again.'

The man sat up in bed and flung the bedclothes from his quaking limbs. 'Good God, you are mad!' he cried aghast[28].

'Get it,' she panted; 'get it quickly, and wish – Oh, my boy, my boy!'

Her husband **struck a match** and lit the candle. 'Get back to bed,' he said, unsteadily. 'You don't know what you are saying.'

'We had the first wish granted,' said the old woman, feverishly; 'why not the second.'

28 shocked and upset

'A coincidence,' stammered the old man.

'Go and get it and wish,' cried the old woman, quivering with excitement.

The old man turned and regarded her, and his voice shook. 'He has been dead ten days, and besides he – I would not tell you else, but – I could only recognize him by his clothing. If he was too terrible for you to see then, how now?'

'Bring him back,' cried the old woman, and dragged him toward the door. 'Do you think I fear the child I have nursed?'

He went down in the darkness, and felt his way to the parlour, and then to the mantelpiece. The talisman was in its place, and a horrible fear that the unspoken wish might bring his mutilated son before him ere[29] he could escape from the room seized upon him, and he caught his breath as he found that he had lost the direction of the door. His brow cold with sweat, he felt his way round the table, and groped along the wall until he found himself in the small passage with the **unwholesome** thing in his hand.

Even his wife's face seemed changed as he entered the room. It was white and expectant, and to his fears seemed to have an unnatural look upon it. He was afraid of her.

'Wish!' she cried, in a strong voice.

'It is foolish and wicked,' he faltered.

'Wish!' repeated his wife.

He raised his hand. 'I wish my son alive again.'

The talisman fell to the floor, and he regarded it fearfully. Then he sank trembling into a chair as the old woman, with burning eyes, walked to the window and raised the blind.

He sat until he was chilled with the cold, glancing occasionally at the figure of the old woman peering through the window. The candle end, which had burnt below the rim of the china candlestick, was throwing pulsating shadows on the ceiling and walls, until, with a flicker larger than the rest, it expired. The old man, with an unspeakable sense of relief at the failure of the talisman, crept back to his bed, and a minute or two afterward the old woman came silently and apathetically beside him.

29 *old-fashioned:* before

Neither spoke, but both lay silently listening to the ticking of the clock. A stair creaked, and a squeaky mouse scurried noisily through the wall. The darkness was oppressive, and after lying for some time **screwing up his courage**, the husband took the box of matches, and striking one, went downstairs for a candle.

At the foot of the stairs the match went out, and he paused to strike another, and at the same moment a knock, so quiet and stealthy as to be scarcely audible, sounded on the front door.

The matches fell from his hand. He stood motionless, his breath suspended until the knock was repeated. Then he turned and fled swiftly back to his room, and closed the door behind him. A third knock sounded through the house.

'What's that?' cried the old woman, starting up.

'A rat,' said the old man, in shaking tones. 'A rat. It passed me on the stairs.'

His wife sat up in bed listening. A loud knock resounded through the house.

'It's Herbert!' she screamed. 'It's Herbert!'

She ran to the door, but her husband was before her, and catching her by the arm, held her tightly.

'What are you going to do?' he whispered hoarsely.

'It's my boy; it's Herbert!' she cried, struggling mechanically. 'I forgot it was two miles away. What are you holding me for? Let go. I must open the door.'

'For God's sake, don't let it in,' cried the old man trembling.

'You're afraid of your own son,' she cried, struggling. 'Let me go. I'm coming, Herbert; I'm coming.'

There was another knock, and another. The old woman with a sudden wrench broke free and ran from the room. Her husband followed to the landing, and called after her appealingly as she hurried downstairs. He heard the chain rattle back and the bottom bolt drawn slowly and stiffly from the socket. Then the old woman's voice, strained and panting.

'The bolt,' she cried loudly. 'Come down. I can't reach it.'

But her husband was on his hands and knees groping wildly on the floor in search of the paw. If he could only find it before the thing outside got in. A perfect fusillade of knocks reverberated through the house, and he heard the scraping of a chair as his wife put it down in the passage against the door. He heard the creaking of the bolt as it came slowly back, and at the same moment he found the monkey's paw, and frantically breathed his third and last wish.

The knocking ceased suddenly, although the echoes of it were still in the house. He heard the chair drawn back and the door opened. A cold wind rushed up the staircase, and a long loud wail of disappointment and misery from his wife gave him courage to run down to her side, and then to the gate beyond. The street lamp flickering opposite shone on a quiet and deserted road.

Post-reading exercises

Understanding the story

1 Use these questions to help you check that you have understood the story.

Part I

1 What were the family doing at the beginning of the story?
2 What kind of atmosphere was there in the house?
3 What was the weather like outside?
4 Who was their visitor?
5 What stories did he tell them?
6 How did they start talking about the subject of the monkey's paw?
7 Why did the fakir put the spell on the paw? What did he want to prove?
8 What did the sergeant-major wish for?
9 How did the sergeant-major get the paw?
10 Why did he throw it on the fire?
11 Why did he let Mr White keep it?
12 What was his warning to Mr White?
13 Why did Herbert suggest they ask for two hundred pounds?
14 What happened when Mr White made his wish?
15 What is the **irony** in Herbert's words *I bet I never shall*?
16 And in those of his father *There's no harm done*?
17 What did Herbert see in the flames of the dying fire?

Part II

18 What did they talk about at breakfast?
19 Where did Herbert go after breakfast?
20 What was Mrs White expecting the postman to bring?
21 What did he bring?
22 Who was the second visitor?
23 What news did he bring?
24 How did he feel about breaking the news?
25 What did Maw and Meggins want to give Mr and Mrs White? Why?

Part III

26 How long after Herbert's funeral was it when Mrs White remembered the paw?
27 What was Mr White's reaction to his wife's suggestion?
28 How did he feel as he took the paw upstairs?
29 Why did he agree to make a second wish?

30 How did they all feel after the wish had been made?
31 Why did Mr White go downstairs?
32 What did he hear?
33 Why did he run upstairs and close the door?
34 Why did he lie to his wife about the rat?
35 What was she referring to when she said *I forgot it was two miles away?*
36 Why did Mr White try to stop his wife from opening the door? What was he afraid of?
37 What was his third wish?

Language study

Adverbs of manner

The use of adverbs is an important characteristic in the author's style. He uses them to build his characters, create atmosphere and add detail to descriptions.

Use

1 **Look at these examples. Underline all the adverbs in the excerpts below; then answer the questions that follow.**

1 *The fire burned brightly.*
2 *The white-haired old lady knitting placidly by the fire.*
3 *His three listeners leaned forward eagerly.*
4 *Her son, taking it, examined it curiously.*
5 *'It must have been your fancy, father,' said his wife, regarding him anxiously.*
6 *The old man started nervously.*
7 *He was at first strangely silent.*
8 *'Badly hurt .... but he is not in pain'.*

Which adverbs are not describing verbs? What are they describing? Which adverbs are:

(a) only describing the manner in which something is done?
(b) also describing the person's personality or mood?

2 **Now, look at the following sentences. Underline the adverbs of manner, then answer the questions that follow.**

1 *The visitor absentmindedly put his empty glass to his lips and then set it down again.*
2 *'If you don't want it, Morris,' said the old man, 'give it to me.'*
   'I won't,' said his friend doggedly.

3 *His father, smiling shamefacedly at his own credulity, held up the talisman.*

4 *'Well, it's just a bit of what you might call magic, perhaps,' said the sergeant-major off-handedly.*

5 *The old lady started. 'Is anything the matter?' she asked breathlessly. 'Has anything happened to Herbert? What is it? What is it?'*

6 *She ran to the door, but her husband was before her, and catching her by the arm, held her tightly.*
'What are you going to do?' he whispered hoarsely.

Which adverbs describe the person's voice? Of these adverbs which suggests that the person:

(a) is short of breath?

(b) has a sore throat?

3 Match the other adverbs in the sentences in exercise 2, to their meanings below:

(a) stubbornly

(b) without thinking

(c) feeling slightly embarrassed

(d) giving something very little importance

Form and position

4 Many adverbs of manner are formed by adding –ly to an adjective, eg *brightly, placidly* etc. Some adverbs consist of several words – we call these adverbial phrases. Look at the sentences below, and underline any adverbial phrases.

1 *The old man rose with hospitable haste.*

2 *He began to talk, the little family circle regarding with eager interest this visitor from distant parts.*

3 *Mrs White drew back with a grimace.*

4 *The three sat listening in an enthralled fashion.*

5 *He gazed at it in amazement.*

Notice how all the phrases start with a preposition; these are prepositional phrases and are often used as adverbs of manner. Notice the position of the adverb, after both the verb and object. This is the most common position for adverbs of manner, especially when they are prepositional phrases.

Adverbs can also come before the verb as in this example.

hurriedly unfastening the strings of her apron

5 Look at the extracts below. Add the adverbs or adverbial phrases in brackets in an appropriate position.

1 *Mr White looked up just in time to intercept a knowing glance between mother and son.*
(sharply) [page 91]

2 *She was watching the mysterious movements of a man outside, who, peering at the house, appeared to be trying to make up his mind to enter.*
(in an undecided fashion) [page 97]

3 *Mr. White dropped his wife's hand, and rising to his feet, gazed at his visitor.*
(with a look of horror) [page 99]

4 *He started up. 'Where? Where is it? What's the matter?'*
(in alarm) [page 100]

5 *Both lay listening to the ticking of the clock.*
(silently) [page 102]

6 *Then he turned and fled back to his room.*
(swiftly) [page 102]

Adverbs of manner with direct speech

The author also uses adverbs of manner with reporting verbs when reporting direct speech. A large part of the action in the story is told through dialogue, and the adverbs intensify and clarify the emotion behind the words.

6 Look at these examples. Add an adverb from the box to each extract.

| curiously | distinctly | feverishly | hastily | solemnly | soothingly |

1 'Never mind, dear,' said his wife .... ; 'perhaps you'll win the next one.'
2 'What was that you started telling me the other day about a monkey's paw or something, Morris?'
'Nothing,' said the soldier .... 'Leastways, nothing worth hearing.'
3 'Monkey's paw?' said Mrs White ....
4 'Better let it burn,' said the soldier ....
5 'I wish for two hundred pounds,' said the old man ....
6 'We had the first wish granted,' said the old woman, ... ; 'why not the second.'

7 **Prepositional phrases can also be used to describe speech. Add the following phrases to the extracts.**

> in a dazed fashion   in a low voice
> in a strong voice   with sudden and unlooked-for violence

1 'That's the worst of living so far out,' bawled Mr White. [page 91]
2 'He was caught in the machinery,' said the visitor. [page 98]
3 'Caught in the machinery,' repeated Mr White. [page 98]
4 'Wish!' she cried. [page 101]

8 **Look at the extracts in the context of the story. What do the adverbial phrases tell us about the speakers in each extract?**

Reporting direct speech

Dialogue plays an important part in the story and the author uses a variety of reporting verbs: *said, inquired, asked, cried, began, replied, repeated, continued, demanded, stammered, screamed, whispered.*

The reporting verbs usually come either in the middle of the direct speech:

> 'I'd like to go to India,' said the old man, 'just to look around a bit, you know.'
> 'If you must wish,' he said gruffly, 'wish for something sensible.'

Or at the end:

> 'Fancy, I suppose,' he said slowly.
> 'Better let it burn,' said the soldier solemnly.

When the reporting verb is used before the direct speech it usually describes some kind of action that accompanies the speech:

> He shook his head. 'Never mind, though; there's no harm done.'
> He started up in alarm. 'Where? Where is it? What's the matter?'

Look again at the examples. Notice how the position of the verb and subject can be inverted: *said the old man, said the soldier.*

This is only possible in the middle or at the end of the direct speech. It is most common with the verb *said,* but can be used with other verbs too.

> 'And what is there special about it?' inquired Mr White.
> 'I say it did,' replied the other.

It is unusual and considered old-fashioned to use inversion (changing the order of the verb and the subject) with a pronoun such as *he*.

'A trifle,' said he, colouring slightly.

Inversion is usually used with a proper name or a noun. The subject does not have to be a person. Look at these examples.

'Two hundred pounds,' was the answer.
'The first man had his three wishes, yes,' was the reply.

9 **Match the extracts of direct speech below (a–h), with the reporting verbs (1–8).**

(a)	*'Hark at the wind,'*	1	she cried wildly
(b)	*'Mate,'*	2	replied the son
(c)	*'Sergeant-Major Morris,'*	3	said Mr White
(d)	*'And did you really have three wishes granted?'*	4	repeated Mr White, in a dazed fashion
(e)	*'It moved,'*	5	he said quietly
(f)	*'Badly hurt,'*	6	he said, introducing him
(g)	*'Caught in the machinery,'*	7	asked Mrs White
(h)	*'The paw!'*	8	he cried

Multiple-clause sentences

The style of the story is quite simple and direct, compared with other stories in this collection. However, there are also several complicated, multiple-clause sentences.

10 **Look at this example from the beginning of the story, where the three main characters are introduced.**

Father and son were at chess, the former, who possessed ideas about the game involving radical changes, putting his king into such sharp and unnecessary perils that it even provoked comment from the white-haired old lady knitting placidly by the fire. [page 91]

Look at how the sentence can be simplified and broken down into several shorter sentences.

Father and son were playing chess.
The father possessed ideas about the game that involved radical changes.
He put his king into sharp and unnecessary perils.
This even provoked comment from the white haired lady.
She was knitting placidly by the fire.

11 What is the effect created by presenting all the information in one sentence? How does this add to the picture the writer is painting of the family?

12 Look at another sentence, describing the sergeant-major as he settles down to tell his tales of India. Break the sentence down into several shorter, simpler sentences, without losing any of the detail in the description.

At the third glass his eyes got brighter, and he began to talk, the little family circle regarding with eager interest this visitor from distant parts, as he squared his broad shoulders in the chair and spoke of strange scenes and doughty deeds; of wars and plagues and strange peoples. [page 92]

13 Here is a third sentence. It describes the moment when the father makes the first wish. Add commas to the sentence to separate the various clauses. Notice how the complexity of the sentence includes all three members of the family in the act of making the wish.

His father smiling shamefacedly at his own credulity held up the talisman as his son with a solemn face somewhat marred by a wink at his mother sat down at the piano and struck a few impressive chords. [page 95]

Literary analysis

Plot

1 Order the events as they happened.

The sergeant-major came back from India	_____
The sergeant-major inherited the monkey's paw	_____
The sergeant-major made three wishes	_____
Mr White made his first wish	_____
Mr White made his second wish	_____
Mr White made his third wish	_____
The first wish came true	_____
The second wish came true	_____
The third wish came true	_____
Herbert was killed in an accident	_____
Herbert came back from the dead	_____
There was a knocking at the front door	_____

2 Which events take place before the story started? Which events are not actually directly described? What effect does this create?

3 In what way are the following people responsible for Herbert's death?
   - the fakir who cast the spell
   - the sergeant major
   - Herbert himself
   - his father
   - his mother

   Who do you think is most to blame? Why? Why did the fakir cast the spell?
4 What could Mr White have done with his second and third wishes? Do you think the story could have had a happy ending if the family had wished for something else? Could they have changed the wording of the wishes to get what they really wanted?
5 What is the main message of the story?

Character

6 Who are the main characters? What do you know about them? What kind of relationship do they have? Why does this make the story all the more tragic?
7 What does the family represent at the beginning of the story? What about Sergeant-major Morris? What does he represent?
8 The characters are, to a great extent, described through their speech. What do we learn about the four characters from what they say and how they speak?

Narration

9 Is the story told from any one character's point of view? Or is the narrator a detached 'third person'?
10 How would the story have been different if it had been told by the Sergeant-major, or by Mr White?
11 Which of the main events of the story are reported by one of the characters? Which are left to the reader's imagination? What effect does this create?
12 The story ends with the anti-climax of the 'quiet deserted road.' What effect does the end have on you, the reader? What effect will it have on Mr and Mrs White? What does the empty road symbolise?

Atmosphere

13 How does the weather add to the atmosphere? What other factors add to the atmosphere at the beginning of the story? Think of the fire, the flames and the candlelight.
14 Think of the sounds in the night when the second wish comes true. Think of the candles and darkness. How do these add to the atmosphere of suspense and terror?

Style

15 Look again at the opening paragraph of the story. Notice how the writer contrasts the scenes inside and outside the house. What is the atmosphere in the house like? How is the weather typical of a horror story?
16 Think about the game of chess. In what way does the author use it to warn about the tragedy to come? What similarities can we draw between the game of chess and the three wishes?
17 Look at the beginning of the second part. What has changed from the night before? What images does the author use to create this atmosphere of hope and optimism?
18 Look at the opening paragraphs of the third part, after Herbert's death. Notice how the author describes the old couple's sorrow. What are the main images used to describe their sadness in the first paragraph? Do you find these effective?
19 Look at the second paragraph. What are the three nouns that the writer uses to describe their state of mind? Why is it important to create this atmosphere before continuing with the story?
20 Read the last two pages again. Why doesn't the author describe Herbert's mutilated (injured or cut up) body? Notice the pronoun his father uses to refer to him when he pleads with his wife not to let him in. How else does he create the horror and suspense of the final scene? Think of the sounds and the use of everyday objects like the chain and the bolt. Think of the timing of the actions.
21 When the door finally opens, what comes into the house? How does this link back to the opening scene? What does the wind represent?

Guidance to the above literary terms, answer keys to all the exercises and activities, plus a wealth of other reading-practice material, can be found on the student's section of the Macmillan Readers website at: www.macmillanenglish.com/readers.

Smoke Ghost

by Fritz Leiber

About the author

Fritz Leiber was an American writer of horror, fantasy and science fiction stories. He started writing in 1939 and went on to write more than 200 short stories and several novels. He died in 1992. During his life, Leiber won many awards, including the **prestigious** Nebula[1] and Hugo[2] awards.

Fritz Leiber was born in Chicago in 1910. Both his parents were successful Shakespearean actors. After graduating from Chicago University, the young Leiber performed with his father's theatre company for several years before he began writing full-time, in the 1940s. His love for the theatre appeared as a theme in a number of his stories, including the short story *Four Ghosts in Hamlet* and the novel, *A Specter is Haunting Texas*, in which the main character is an actor.

In 1936, he married his first wife, Jonquil Stephens, and in 1938, his son, Justin, was born. The family lived in Hollywood for a while, where Leiber tried to get into film writing. However, they soon returned to Chicago. In 1939, Leiber published his first short story, *Two Sought Adventure*, in a fantasy magazine called *Unknown*. It was the first story in the *Fafhrd and the Gray Mouser* series, epic fantasy adventures that Leiber wrote over the next 50 years of his writing career, and for which he became famous.

In 1969, Leiber's wife Jonquil died. He was deeply upset by her death; he moved to San Francisco, he stopped writing completely for three years, and he became an alcoholic. However, he returned to writing, and set many of his later stories in San Francisco. For a long time, though, he was lonely, and many of his later stories are narrated by sad older men, living alone, like himself. In 1992, he married his long-time friend, Margo Skinner, but only four months later he died, at the age of eighty-one.

Leiber was influenced by various writers in his life. As a young man, he had great respect for H P Lovecraft, the famous American horror and

1 the Nebula Award is given each year for the best science fiction/fantasy fiction published in the USA during the previous two years
2 the Hugo Awards are awarded each year for the best science fiction/fantasy fiction of the previous year

fantasy writer, and they exchanged letters. Leiber considered him to be a mentor (a mental guide or teacher) for him, and he later published several essays about Lovecraft's works. He was also influenced by the great English ghost writer, M R James, and many of his works of horror make references to James's short stories (including *Oh Whistle and I'll Come, My Lad*).

Leiber's horror stories are set in an urban (cities and towns), industrial landscape and he is famous for introducing a new type of ghost to horror literature – an urban ghost that is the spirit of modern American cities. This is the kind of ghost that he described in his novel, *Our Lady of Darkness*, which some people believe is one of the best novels of supernatural terror ever written. It is also the kind of ghost that haunts Catesby Wran in *Smoke Ghost*.

About the story

Smoke Ghost was first published in the magazine, *Unknown*, in October 1941, and was later included in Leiber's first short story collection, *Night's Black Agents*. It is an example of early urban horror and introduced a new kind of ghost, a modern, industrial ghost, born of the dirt and noise and violence of the city.

It is set in Chicago in the early 1940s, which is where Leiber was living at the time.

Background information

Chicago in the 1940s

Chicago is the USA's third-largest city. It is the home to the first skyscraper, and in the 1940s it was highly industrialised. Manufacturing industries still burnt coal and many parts of the city were poor and dirty.

There was a large immigrant community, made up both of European immigrants and large numbers of African American immigrants from the Southern States looking for work in the industries of the North. The black community grew quickly and the city became a centre for jazz music.

In the first half of the century, Chicago was known for its violence, industrial disputes and organised crime. In the 1920s, when the sale of alcohol was illegal, Chicago was the home to Al Capone and his gang.

Chicago's elevated railroad

A large part of the inner-city railway tracks in Chicago are built above street level – these are the 'elevated railroads', known as 'the L' or 'the elevated' by locals. The elevated railroads are one of Chicago's best-known features.

Historical background

In 1941, the world was at war. The USA did not enter the war until after the attack on Pearl Harbour in December 1941, but it was the second world war in Leiber's lifetime.

Summary

It may help you to know something about what happens in the story before you read it. Don't worry, this summary does not tell you how the story ends.

Catesby Wran lives in Chicago. He works in advertising. He lives a normal life until one day, when he is travelling home on the elevated railway, he sees a strange shape on a rooftop: a dark object, which looks like a sack, perhaps full of leaves or soot. Catesby looks for the shape the next day, and sees that it has moved. Each night, as he travels home from work, he looks out for the strange object, and it seems to him that it is moving nearer and slowly changing shape, taking on the form of a face and body.

The next day, at work, Catesby starts to act a little strangely, making strange comments and jokes about ghosts to his secretary, Miss Millick. He becomes obsessive about cleanliness, and it seems to him that his office is full of dirt and soot. He has started to think the shape on the roof is coming to get him.

He realises that his obsession is becoming a problem and he makes an appointment to see a psychiatrist. He's hoping that the psychiatrist will help him forget these visions and strange thoughts. He tells the psychiatrist about his past – when he was a child, he, his mother and others believed he had psychic powers, that he could see through walls and read people's minds. When the psychiatrist asks him if he has started seeing things again, Catesby prepares to tell the psychiatrist about the shape on the roof. However, he realises that the psychiatrist isn't listening to him – he is looking out of the window, and he is scared by what he sees: a black face looking in at him. Catesby leaves without telling the psychiatrist about the shape on the roof.

Catesby does not go straight home as planned. He walks around the streets and eventually goes back to his office. He is convinced that the shape is following him. Catesby is sitting in his office in the dark, wondering what the shape wants from him, when the phone rings. It is his wife. She's been worried about him. He doesn't usually work late at the office, and their son has been frightened by a black face he saw at his window. Catesby gets up to go home, but when he calls the lift, he looks down the shaft and sees a black face staring up at him.

Pre-reading exercises

Key vocabulary

This section will help you familiarise yourself with some of the more specific vocabulary used in the story. You may want to use it to help you before you start reading, or as a revision exercise after you've finished the story.

Describing the city

To understand the story and the nature of the ghost that haunts it, it is important to understand the writer's vision of the city where the story takes place. The writer provides detailed descriptions of the sights, sounds and places that he associates most strongly with the city.

1 **Read the extracts below and decide if the words in bold are describing people, places, sounds or things. Then, match the words to the definitions/descriptions that follow each extract.**

> (a) *I mean a ghost from the world today, with the* **soot** *(a) of the factories on its face and the* **pounding** *(b) of machinery in its soul. The kind that would haunt* **coal yards** *(c) and slip around at night through deserted office buildings like this one.*

1 an area where coal was kept and stored before being used or sold

2 a dirty, black powder that is produced when you burn coal or wood
3 the sound of repeated hard hits or loud noise

> (b) *He turned away and stared out into the gray **down-town** (a) atmosphere that rolled in from the **railroad yards** (b) and the **mills** (c).*

1 a place where trains are kept
2 factories
3 (US) city centre

> (c) *A **dingy** (a), melancholy little world of **tar-paper** (b), **tarred gravel** (c) and smoky brick. **Rusty tin chimneys** (d) with odd conical hats suggested abandoned listening posts... Superficially it was like ten thousand other **drab** (e) city roofs.*

1 small stones held together by a thick, black liquid made of coal
2 not colourful or interesting
3 a tube that takes smoke from a fire up through a building and out through the roof, made of a soft light metal that has been damaged by rain and turned a dark red or brown
4 a roof covering made from card and a thick, black liquid made from coal (often used to cover roads)
5 dark, in an unpleasant way, and often looking dirty

Dirt

Dirt is probably the one most important characteristics of both the city and the ghost.

2 Look at the extracts below. All the words in bold refer to dirt in some way. Read the extracts and answer the questions below.

> *There were **smudges** on the glass.*
> *He was straining his eyes through the **murky** twilight, determined to take in every detail.*
> *He frowned worriedly at the almost **inky smears**.*
> *He jerked open a drawer, snatched out a **rag,** hastily **swabbed off** the desk, crumpled the **rag** into a ball and tossed it back.*
> *Its colour and texture, and the **grimy stains** around it, suggested that it was filled with coal dust.*

a) Which three nouns mean *dirty marks?*

b) Which adjective suggests that the mark is black?

c) Which verb means *to wash or clean something?*

d) Which noun describes an object used for cleaning?

e) Which adjective suggests that you can't see clearly because of the dirt?

3 Choose the correct word to complete the following sentences.

1 She looked into the **smeared/murky** water, but could see nothing.

2 The wine glass fell onto her dress, leaving a large red **stain/rag.**

3 She kissed him, leaving a large **smudge/swab** of lipstick on his cheek.

4 The stars were just starting to appear in the **inky/murky** night sky.

Nervous reactions

All the characters show some degree of nervousness at some point in the story. The writer uses a number of different verbs, nouns and adjectives to describe their nervous reactions.

4 Look at the list below, and then choose a word or phrase to replace the words in bold in the extracts (a–i).

Definitions

all at sea PHRASE confused and not sure what to do

blush verb if you blush, your face turns red because you feel embarrassed or ashamed

gasping *mainly literary* noun or verb to breathe in suddenly/ a sudden noisy breath, caused by surprise, shock or pain

jumpy adj *informal* nervous or worried

on edge PHRASE unable to relax because you are worried about something

shiver noun or verb a slight shaking movement / to shake slightly, because you are cold, frightened or excited

squirm verb to look or feel embarrassed

stammer verb to keep repeating a sound and have difficulty in saying certain words because of a speech problem, or because of nerves

titter noun or verb a quiet laugh / to laugh quietly, especially because you are nervous or embarrassed

twitch /noun or verb (to make) a sudden, slight, uncontrolled movement of your body

worked up adj upset, angry or excited

(a) *Just this morning he had quickly turned around and asked, 'Have you ever seen a ghost, Miss Millick?' And she had* **laughed** *nervously.*

(b) *'Have you ever thought what a ghost of our times would look like Miss Millick? …'*
Miss Millick gave a little, self-conscious **shaking movement** and said, 'That would be terrible.'

(c) *Miss Millick* **looked embarrassed** *and read back her shorthand, like the books said you should when there was a pause.*

(d) *She hung her head and might even have* **turned red** *if she hadn't felt so* **uncertain***.*

(e) *'So, you find yourself growing nervous and …er…***worried** *…'*

(f) *The doctor slammed down the window and said in a voice whose smoothness was marred[3] by a slight, persistent* **noisy breathing***, 'I hope I haven't alarmed you.'*

(g) *'Why, Mr Wran,' she* **said with difficulty***, 'I didn't know you were here.'*

(h) *After a while she began to* **make sudden, uncontrolled movements.** *Small noises came from her throat and her eyelids edged open.*

(i) *I got* **emotional and nervous***.*

Main themes

Before you read the story, you may want to think about some of its main themes. The questions will help you think about the story as you're reading it for the first time. There is more discussion of the main themes in the *Literary analysis* section after the story.

The nature of a modern, urban ghost

One of the main themes of the story is the exploration of the nature of a modern, urban ghost. The ghost, or projection, described in the story is a representation of modern, urban, industrialised society. It is made of the dirt and noise and grim greyness of the skyscrapers and the coal-burning factories of the city.

---

3 to spoil something, to affect it in a negative way

5 As you read, think about what the ghost represents. What does it tell us about the great industrial cities of the 1940s? Consider the following questions:

a) Is life in a city very different today?

b) What would be the characteristics of a ghost in a 21st century city? Would it be very different from the Smoke Ghost?

The first half of the 20th century

Leiber **paints a bleak picture** of life in the 20th century. He calls it the *century of hate and heavy industry and total wars.*

6 As you read, consider these questions:

a) What are the pressures and problems of life for people living in Leiber's Chicago of the 1940s?

b) How does the prospect of war affect them?

c) What similarities are there (if any) with the world in the first half of the 21st century?

Smoke Ghost

by Fritz Leiber

Miss Millick wondered just what had happened to Mr Wran. He kept making the strangest remarks when she took dictation. Just this morning he had quickly turned around and asked, "Have you ever seen a ghost, Miss Millick?" And she had tittered nervously and replied, "When I was a girl there was a thing in white that used to come out of the closet in the attic bedroom when I slept there, and moan. Of course it was just my imagination. I was frightened of lots of things." And he had said, "I don't mean that kind of ghost. I mean a ghost from the world today, with the soot of the factories on its face and the pounding of machinery in its soul. The kind that would haunt coal yards and slip around at night through deserted office buildings like this one. A real ghost. Not something out of books." And she hadn't known what to say.

He'd never been like this before. Of course he might be joking, but it didn't sound that way. Vaguely Miss Millick wondered whether he mightn't be seeking some sort of sympathy from her. Of course, Mr Wran was married and had a little child, but that didn't prevent her from having daydreams. The daydreams were not very exciting, still they helped fill up her mind. But now he was asking her another of those unprecedented questions.

"Have you ever thought what a ghost of our times would look like, Miss Millick? Just picture it. A smoky composite face with the hungry anxiety of the unemployed, the neurotic restlessness of the person without purpose, the jerky[4] tension of the high-pressure metropolitan worker, the uneasy resentment of the striker, the callous[5] opportunism of the scab[6], the aggressive

4 a jerky movement consists of several separate, short movements
5 without feelings
6 *offensive:* a person who continues to work when the other workers are on strike

whine of the panhandler[7], the inhibited terror of the bombed civilian, and a thousand other twisted emotional patterns. Each one overlying and yet blending with the other, like a pile of semitransparent masks?"

Miss Millick gave a little self-conscious shiver and said, "That would be terrible. What an awful thing to think of."

She peered furtively across the desk. She remembered having heard that there had been something impressively abnormal about Mr Wran's childhood, but she couldn't recall what it was. If only she could do something – laugh at his mood or ask him what was really wrong. She shifted the extra pencils in her left hand and mechanically traced over some of the shorthand curlicues[8] in her notebook.

"Yet, that's just what such a ghost or vitalized projection[9] would look like, Miss Millick," he continued, smiling in a tight way. "It would grow out of the real world. It would reflect the tangled, sordid, vicious things. All the **loose ends**. And it would be very grimy. I don't think it would seem white or wispy, or favour graveyards. It wouldn't moan. But it would **mutter** unintelligibly, and twitch at your sleeve. Like a sick, surly ape. What would such a thing want from a person, Miss Millick? Sacrifice? Worship? Or just fear? What could you do to stop it from troubling you?"

Miss Millick giggled nervously. There was an expression beyond her powers of definition in Mr Wran's ordinary, flat-cheeked, thirtyish face, silhouetted against the dusty window. He turned away and stared out into the gray[10] down-town atmosphere that rolled in from the railroad yards and the mills. When he spoke again his voice sounded far away.

"Of course, being immaterial, it couldn't hurt you physically – at first. You'd have to be peculiarly sensitive to see it, or be aware of it at all. But it would begin to influence your actions. Make you do this. Stop you from doing that. Although only a

7 US, *informal:* beggar, a person who asks for money on the street
8 a curl or twist used as a decoration
9 a projection (an idea you feel strongly about) that has come to life
10 US *spelling:* grey

projection, it would gradually **get its hooks into** the world of things as they are. Might even get control of suitably vacuous minds. Then it could hurt whomever it wanted."

Miss Millick squirmed and read back her shorthand, like the books said you should do when there was a pause. She became aware of the failing light and wished Mr Wran would ask her to turn on the overhead[11]. She felt scratchy, as if soot were sifting down on to her skin.

"It's a rotten world, Miss Millick," said Mr Wran, talking at the window. "Fit for another **morbid** growth of superstition. It's time the ghosts, or whatever you call them, took over and began a rule of fear. They'd be no worse than men."

"But" – Miss Millick's diaphragm jerked, making her titter inanely – "of course, there aren't any such things as ghosts."

Mr Wran turned around.

"Of course there aren't, Miss Millick," he said in a loud, patronizing voice, as if she had been doing the talking rather than he. "Science and common sense and psychiatry all go to prove it."

She hung her head and might even have blushed if she hadn't felt so all at sea. Her leg muscles twitched, making her stand up, although she hadn't intended to. She aimlessly rubbed her hand along the edge of the desk.

"Why, Mr Wran, look what I got off your desk," she said, showing him a heavy smudge. There was a note of clumsily playful reproof in her voice. "No wonder the copy I bring you always gets so black. Somebody ought to talk to those scrubwomen.[12] They're **skimping**[13] on your room."

She wished he would make some normal joking reply. But instead he drew back and his face hardened.

"Well, to get back," he rapped out harshly, and began to dictate.

When she was gone, he jumped up, dabbed his finger experimentally at the smudged part of the desk, frowned

11 overhead light
12 *US, old-fashioned:* cleaners
13 to not use, do or provide enough of something

worriedly at the almost inky smears. He jerked open a drawer, snatched out a rag[14], hastily swabbed off[15] the desk, crumpled the rag into a ball and tossed it back. There were three or four other rags in the drawer, each impregnated[16] with soot.

Then he went over to the window and peered out anxiously through the dusk, his eyes searching the panorama of roofs, fixing on each chimney and water tank.

"It's a neurosis. Must be. Compulsions. Hallucinations," he muttered to himself in a tired, **distraught** voice that would have made Miss Millick gasp. "It's that damned mental abnormality **cropping up** in a new form. Can't be any other explanation. But it's so damned real. Even the soot. Good thing I'm seeing the psychiatrist. I don't think I could force myself to get on the elevated railway tonight." His voice trailed off, he rubbed his eyes, and his memory automatically started to grind.

It had all begun on the elevated[17]. There was a particular little sea of roofs he had grown into the habit of glancing at just as the packed car carrying him homeward **lurched** around a turn. A dingy, melancholy little world of tar-paper, tarred gravel and smoky brick. Rusty tin chimneys with odd conical hats suggested abandoned listening posts. There was a washed-out advertisement of some ancient patent medicine on the nearest wall. Superficially it was like ten thousand other drab city roofs. But he always saw it around dusk, either in the smoky half-light, or tinged with red by the flat rays of a dirty sunset, or covered by ghostly windblown white sheets of rain-splash, or patched with blackish snow; and it seemed unusually **bleak** and suggestive; almost beautifully ugly though in no sense picturesque; dreary, but meaningful. Unconsciously it came to symbolize for Catesby Wran certain disagreeable aspects of the frustrated, frightened century in which he lived, the jangled[18] century of hate and heavy industry and total wars. The quick daily glance into the

14 piece of cloth, often made from old clothes or fabric
15 wiped clean, with a cloth
16 soaked with, completely covered in (usually a liquid)
17 the elevated railroad, a rail system built above street level
18 if something jangles someone's nerves it makes them nervous

half darkness became an integral part of his life. Oddly, he never saw it in the morning, for it was then his habit to sit on the other side of the car, his head buried in the paper.

One evening toward winter he noticed what seemed to be a shapeless black sack lying on the third roof from the tracks. He did not think about it. It merely registered as an addition to the well-known scene and his memory stored away the impression for further reference. Next evening, however, he decided he had been mistaken in one detail. The object was a roof nearer than he had thought. Its colour and texture, and the grimy stains around it, suggested that it was filled with coal dust, which was hardly reasonable. Then, too, the following evening it seemed to have been blown against a rusty ventilator by the wind – which could hardly have happened if it were at all heavy. Perhaps it was filled with leaves. Catesby was surprised to find himself anticipating his next daily glance with a minor note of apprehension. There was something unwholesome in the posture of the thing that stuck in his mind – a bulge in the sacking that suggested a misshaped head peering around the ventilator. And his apprehension was justified, for that evening the thing was on the nearest roof, though on the farther side, looking as if it had just **flopped** down over the low brick parapet[19].

Next evening the sack was gone. Catesby was annoyed at the momentary feeling of relief that went through him, because the whole matter seemed too unimportant to warrant feelings of any sort. What difference did it make if his imagination had played tricks on him, and he'd fancied that the object was slowly crawling and **hitching** itself closer across the roofs? That was the way any normal imagination worked. He deliberately chose to disregard the fact that there were reasons for thinking his imagination was by no means a normal one. As he walked home from the elevated, however, he found himself wondering whether the sack was really gone. He seemed to recall a vague, smudgy trail leading across the gravel to the nearer side of the roof, which was masked by a parapet. For an instant an unpleasant

19 a low wall at the edge of something high such as a roof

picture formed in his mind – that of an inky, humped creature crouched behind the parapet, waiting.

The next time he felt the familiar grating lurch of the car, he caught himself trying not to look out. That angered him. He turned his head quickly. When he turned it back, his compact face was definitely pale. There had been only time for a fleeting rearward[20] glance at the escaping roof. Had he actually seen in silhouette the upper part of a head of some sort peering over the parapet? Nonsense, he told himself. And even if he had seen something, there were a thousand explanations which did not involve the supernatural or even true hallucination. Tomorrow he would take a good look and clear up the whole matter. If necessary, he would visit the roof personally, though he hardly knew where to find it and disliked in any case the idea of **pampering** a silly fear.

He did not relish the walk home from the elevated that evening and visions of the thing disturbed his dreams, and were in and out of his mind all next day at the office. It was then that he first began to relieve his nerves by making jokingly serious remarks about the supernatural to Miss Millick, who seemed properly mystified. It was on the same day, too, that he became aware of a growing antipathy to grime and soot. Everything he touched seemed gritty[21], and he found himself mopping and wiping at his desk like an old lady with a morbid fear of germs. He reasoned that there was no real change in his office, and that he'd just now become sensitive to the dirt that had always been there, but there was no denying an increasing nervousness. Long before the car reached the curve, he was straining his eyes through the murky twilight, determined to take in every detail.

Afterward he realized he must have given a muffled cry of some sort, for the man beside him looked at him curiously, and the woman ahead gave him an unfavourable stare. Conscious of his own pallor and uncontrollable trembling, he stared back at them hungrily, trying to regain the feeling of security he had completely lost. They were the usual reassuringly wooden-faced

20 *formal:* in or towards the back of something, backwards
21 as if it had sand, or particles of dirt, on it

people everyone rides home with on the elevated. But suppose he had pointed out to one of them what he had seen – that sodden[22], distorted face of sacking and coal dust, that boneless paw[23] which waved **back and forth**, unmistakably in his direction, as if reminding him of a future appointment – he involuntarily shut his eyes tight. His thoughts were racing ahead to tomorrow evening. He pictured this same windowed oblong of light and packed humanity surging around the curve – then an opaque monstrous form leaping out from the roof in a parabolic swoop – an unmentionable face pressed close against the window, smearing it with wet coal dust – huge paws fumbling sloppily at the glass –

Somehow he managed to turn off his wife's anxious inquiries. Next morning he reached a decision and made an appointment for that evening with a psychiatrist a friend had told him about. It cost him a considerable effort, for Catesby had a well-grounded distaste for anything dealing with psychological abnormality. Visiting a psychiatrist meant raking up[24] an episode in his past which he had never fully described even to his wife. Once he had made the decision, however, he felt considerably relieved. The psychiatrist, he told himself, would clear everything up. He could almost fancy him saying, "Merely a bad case of nerves. However, you must consult the oculist[25] whose name I'm writing down for you, and you must take two of these pills in water every four hours," and so on. It was almost comforting, and made the coming revelation he would have to make seem less painful.

But as the smoky dusk rolled in, his nervousness had returned and he had let his joking mystification of Miss Millick run away with him until he had realized he wasn't frightening anyone but himself.

He would have to keep his imagination under better control, he told himself, as he continued to peer out restlessly at the massive, murky shapes of the downtown office buildings. Why,

22 completely wet
23 the foot of an animal
24 *informal:* to mention something unpleasant that happened in the past and that
    someone else doesn't want to talk about
25 *US:* an eye specialist

he had spent the whole afternoon building up a kind of neo-medieval cosmology of superstition. It wouldn't do. He realized then that he had been standing at the window much longer than he'd thought, for the glass panel in the door was dark and there was no noise coming from the outer office. Miss Millick and the rest must have gone home.

It was then he made the discovery that there would have been no special reason for **dreading** the swing around the curve that night. It was, as it happened, a horrible discovery. For, on the shadowed roof across the street and four stories below, he saw the thing huddle and roll across the gravel and, after one upward look of recognition, merge into the blackness beneath the water tank.

As he hurriedly collected his things and made for the elevator[26], fighting the panicky impulse to run, he began to think of hallucination and mild psychosis as very desirable conditions. For better or for worse, he **pinned all his hopes** on the psychiatrist.

———

"So you find yourself growing nervous and … er … jumpy, as you put it," said Dr Trevethick, smiling with dignified geniality. "Do you notice any more definite physical symptoms? Pain? Headache? Indigestion?"

Catesby shook his head and wet his lips. "I'm especially nervous while riding in the elevated," he murmured swiftly.

"I see. We'll discuss that more fully. But I'd like you first to tell me about something you mentioned earlier. You said there was something about your childhood that might predispose you to nervous ailments. As you know, the early years are critical ones in the development of an individual's behaviour pattern."

Catesby studied the yellow reflections of frosted globes[27] in the dark surface of the desk. The palm of his left hand aimlessly rubbed the thick nap[28] of the armchair. After a while he raised

26 US: a lift
27 round covers for lights; these ones are 'frosted' – glass that has a rough surface so that you cannot see clearly through it
28 material

his head and looked straight into the doctor's small brown eyes.

"From perhaps my third to my ninth year," he began, choosing the words with care, "I was what you might call a sensory prodigy."

The doctor's expression did not change. "Yes?" he inquired politely.

"What I mean is that I was supposed to be able to see through walls, read letters through envelopes and books through their covers, fence and play ping-pong blindfolded, find things that were buried, read thoughts." The words tumbled out.

"And could you?" The doctor's voice was toneless.

"I don't know. I don't suppose so," answered Catesby, long-lost emotions flooding back into his voice. "It's all confused now. I thought I could, but then they were always encouraging me. My mother ... was ... well ... interested in psychic phenomena. I was ... exhibited. I seem to remember seeing things other people couldn't. As if most opaque objects were transparent. But I was very young. I didn't have any scientific criteria for judgment."

He was reliving it now. The darkened rooms. The earnest assemblages of gawking[29], **prying** adults. Himself alone on a little platform, lost in a straight-backed wooden chair. The black silk handkerchief over his eyes. His mother's coaxing, insistent questions. The whispers. The gasps. His own hate of the whole business, mixed with hunger for the adulation of adults. Then the scientists from the university, the experiments, the big test. The reality of those memories engulfed him and momentarily made him forget the reason why he was disclosing them to a stranger.

"Do I understand that your mother tried to make use of you as a medium for communicating with the ... er ... other world?"

Catesby nodded eagerly.

"She tried to, but she couldn't. When it came to getting in touch with the dead, I was a complete failure. All I could do – or thought I could do – was see real, existing, three-dimensional objects beyond the vision of normal people. Objects anyone

29 *mainly US, also 'gawp'*: to look at someone or something for a long time, often in a rude or stupid way, and usually with your mouth open in surprise

could have seen except for distance, obstruction, or darkness. It was always a disappointment to mother."

He could hear her sweetish, patient voice saying, "Try again, dear, just this once. Katie was your aunt. She loved you. Try to hear what she's saying." And he had answered, "I can see a woman in a blue dress standing on the other side of Dick's house." And she had replied, "Yes, I know dear. But that's not Katie. Katie's a spirit. Try again. Just this once, dear." The doctor's voice gently jarred him back into the softly gleaming office.

"You mentioned scientific criteria for judgement, Mr Wran. As far as you know did anyone ever try to apply them to you?"

Catesby's nod was emphatic.

"They did. When I was eight, two young psychologists from the university got interested in me. I guess they did it for a joke at first, and I remember being very determined to show them I **amounted to** something. Even now I seem to recall how the note of polite superiority and amused sarcasm drained out of their voices. I suppose they decided at first that it was very clever trickery, but somehow they persuaded mother to let them try me out under controlled conditions. There were lots of tests that seemed very businesslike after mother's slipshod[30] little exhibitions. They found I was clairvoyant – or so they thought. I got worked up and on edge. They were going to demonstrate my supernormal sensory powers to the university psychology faculty. For the first time I began to worry about whether I'd come through. Perhaps they kept me going at too hard a pace, I don't know. At any rate, when the test came, I couldn't do a thing. Everything became opaque. I got desperate and made things up out of my imagination. I lied. In the end I failed utterly, and I believe the two young psychologists **got into a lot of hot water** as a result."

He could hear the brusque, bearded man saying, "You've been taken in by a child, Flaxman, a mere child. I'm greatly disturbed. You've put yourself on the same plane as common **charlatans**. Gentlemen, I ask you to banish from your minds this whole sorry episode. It must never be referred to." He **winced**

30 *old-fashioned:* done in a careless way

at the recollection of his feeling of guilt. But at the same time he was beginning to feel exhilarated and almost light-hearted. **Unburdening** his long-repressed memories had altered his whole viewpoint. The episodes on the elevated began to take on what seemed their proper proportions as merely the bizarre workings of **overwrought** nerves and an overly suggestible mind. The doctor, he anticipated confidently, would disentangle the obscure subconscious causes, whatever they might be. And the whole business would be finished off quickly, just as his childhood experience – which was beginning to seem a little ridiculous now – had been finished off.

"From that day on," he continued, "I never exhibited a trace of my supposed powers. My mother was frantic and tried to sue the university. I had something like a nervous breakdown. Then the divorce was granted, and my father got custody of me. He did his best to make me forget it. We went on long outdoor vacations and did a lot of athletics, associated with normal matter-of-fact people. I went to business college eventually. I'm in advertising now. But," Catesby paused, "now that I'm having nervous symptoms, I've wondered if there mightn't be a connection. It's not a question of whether I was really clairvoyant or not. Very likely my mother taught me a lot of unconscious deceptions, good enough to fool even young psychology instructors. But don't you think it may have some important bearing on my present condition?"

For several moments the doctor regarded him with a professional frown. Then he said quietly, "And is there some … er … more specific connection between your experiences then and now? Do you by any chance find that you are once again beginning to … er … see things?"

Catesby swallowed. He had felt an increasing eagerness to unburden himself of his fears, but it was not easy to make a beginning, and the doctor's **shrewd** question **rattled** him. He forced himself to concentrate. The thing he thought he had seen on the roof **loomed up** before his inner eye with unexpected vividness. Yet it did not frighten him. He groped for words.

Then he saw that the doctor was not looking at him but over

his shoulder. Color was draining out of the doctor's face and his eyes did not seem so small. Then the doctor sprang to his feet, walked past Catesby, threw up the window and peered into the darkness.

As Catesby rose, the doctor slammed down the window and said in a voice whose smoothness was marred by a slight, persistent gasping, "I hope I haven't alarmed you. I saw the face of ... er ... a Negro[31] prowler on the fire escape. I must have frightened him, for he seems to have gotten[32] out of sight in a hurry. Don't give it another thought. Doctors are frequently bothered by *voyeurs* ... er ... Peeping Toms."

"A Negro?" asked Catesby, moistening his lips.

The doctor laughed nervously, "I imagine so, though my first odd impression was that it was a white man in blackface[33]. You see, the color[34] didn't seem to have any brown in it. It was dead-black."

Catesby moved toward the window. There were smudges on the glass. "It's quite all right, Mr Wran." The Doctor's voice had acquired a sharp note of impatience, as if he were trying hard to reassume his professional authority. "Let's continue our conversation. I was asking you if you were" – he made a face – "seeing things."

Catesby's whirling thoughts slowed down and locked into place. "No, I'm not seeing anything that other people don't see, too. And I think I'd better go now. I've been keeping you too long." He disregarded the doctor's half-hearted gesture of denial. "I'll phone you about the physical examination. In a way you've already **taken a big load off my mind**." He smiled woodenly. "Goodnight, Dr Trevethick."

––––––

Catesby Wran's mental state was a peculiar one. His eyes searched every angular shadow, he glanced sideways down each chasm-like alley and barren basement passage-way, and kept

31 *old-fashioned:* a black person of African decent; in the 1940s it was a normal, neutral term, but it has since come to be considered offensive in most contexts
32 US: the past participle of *get* in British English is *got*
33 a white person wearing make-up in order to look black
34 US *spelling:* colour

stealing looks at the irregular line of roofs, yet he was hardly conscious of where he was going. He pushed away the thoughts that came into his mind, and kept moving. He became aware of a slight sense of security as he turned into a lighted street where there were people and high buildings and blinking signs. After a while he found himself in the dim lobby[35] of the structure that housed his office. Then he realized why he couldn't go home, why he daren't go home – after what had happened at the office of Dr Trevethick.

"Hello, Mr Wran," said the night elevator man, a burly figure in overalls, sliding open the grille-work door to the old-fashioned cage. "I didn't know you were working nights now, too."

Catesby stepped in automatically. "Sudden rush of orders," he murmured inanely. "Some stuff that has to be gotten out."

The cage creaked to a stop at the top floor. "Be working very late, Mr Wran?"

He nodded vaguely, watched the car slide out of sight, found his keys, swiftly crossed the outer office, and entered his own. His hand went out to the light switch, but then the thought occurred to him that the two lighted windows, standing out against the dark bulk of the building, would indicate his whereabouts and serve as a goal toward which something could crawl and climb. He moved his chair so that the back was against the wall and sat down in the semidarkness. He did not remove his overcoat.

For a long time he sat there motionless, listening to his own breathing and the faraway sounds from the streets below: the thin metallic surge of the crosstown streetcar[36], the farther one of the elevated, faint lonely cries and honkings[37], indistinct rumblings. Words he had spoken to Miss Millick in nervous jest[38] came back to him with the bitter taste of truth. He found himself unable to reason critically or connectedly, but by their own volition thoughts rose up into his mind and **gyrated** slowly and rearranged themselves with the inevitable movement of planets.

35 *mainly US*: the area just inside a hotel, theatre or other large building
36 *US*: tram
37 the sound of car horns
38 *old-fashioned*: if you say something in jest, you do not mean it seriously

Gradually his mental picture of the world was transformed. No longer a world of material atoms and empty space, but a world in which the bodiless existed and moved according to its own obscure laws or unpredictable impulses. The new picture illuminated with dreadful clarity certain general facts which had always **bewildered** and troubled him and from which he had tried to hide: the inevitability of hate and war, the diabolically timed mischances[39] which wreck the best of human intentions, the walls of wilful misunderstanding that divide one man from another, the eternal vitality of cruelty and ignorance and greed. They seemed appropriate now, necessary parts of the picture. And superstition only a kind of wisdom.

Then his thoughts returned to himself and the question he had asked Miss Millick, "What would such a thing want from a person? Sacrifices? Worship? Or just fear? What could you do to stop it from troubling you?" It had become a practical question.

With an explosive jangle, the phone began to ring. "Cate, I've been trying everywhere to get you," said his wife. "I never thought you'd be at the office. What are you doing? I've been worried."

He said something about work.

"You'll be home right away?" came the faint anxious question. "I'm a little frightened. Ronny just had a scare. It woke him up. He kept pointing to the window saying, "Black man, black man." Of course it's something he dreamed. But I'm frightened. You will be home? What's that, dear? Can't you hear me?"

"I will, right away," he said. Then he was out of the office, buzzing the night bell and peering down the shaft.

———

He saw it peering up the shaft at him from the deep shadows three floors below, the sacking face pressed against the iron grille-work. It started up the stair at a shockingly swift, shambling gait, vanishing temporarily from sight as it swung into the second corridor below.

Catesby clawed at the door to the office, realized he had not locked it, pushed it in, slammed and locked it behind him,

39 *mainly literary*: bad luck, or something that is caused by bad luck

retreated to the other side of the room, **cowered** between the filing cases and the wall. His teeth were clicking. He heard the groan of the rising cage. A silhouette darkened the frosted glass of the door, blotting out part of the grotesque reverse of the company name. After a little the door opened.

The big-globed overhead light flared on and, standing inside the door, her hand on the switch, was Miss Millick.

"Why, Mr Wran," she stammered vacuously, "I didn't know you were here. I'd just come in to do some extra typing after the movie. I didn't … but the lights weren't on. What were you – "

He stared at her. He wanted to shout in relief, grab hold of her, talk rapidly. He realized he was grinning hysterically.

"Why, Mr Wran, what's happened to you?" she asked embarrassedly, ending with a stupid titter. "Are you feeling sick? Isn't there something I can do for you?"

He shook his head jerkily and managed to say, "No, I'm just leaving. I was doing some extra work myself."

"But you *look* sick," she insisted, and walked over toward him. He inconsequentially realized she must have stepped in mud, for her high-heeled shoes left neat black prints.

"Yes, I'm sure you must be sick. You're so terribly pale." She sounded like an enthusiastic, incompetent nurse. Her face brightened with a sudden inspiration. "I've got something in my bag, that'll fix you up right away," she said. "It's for indigestion."

She fumbled at her stuffed oblong purse. He noticed that she was absent-mindedly holding it shut with one hand while she tried to open it with the other. Then, under his very eyes, he saw her bend back the thick prongs of metal locking the purse as if they were tinfoil, or as if her fingers had become a pair of steel pliers.

Instantly his memory recited the worlds he had spoken to Miss Millick that afternoon. "It couldn't hurt you physically – at first … gradually get its hooks into the world … might even get control of suitably vacuous minds. Then it could hurt whomever it wanted." A sickish, cold feeling grew inside him. He began to edge toward the door.

But Miss Millick was ahead of him.

"You don't have to wait, Fred," she called. "Mr Wran's decided to stay a while longer."

The door to the cage shut with a mechanical rattle. The cage creaked. Then she turned around in the door.

"Why, Mr Wran," she gurgled reproachfully, "I just couldn't think of letting you go home now. I'm sure you're terribly unwell. Why, you might collapse in the street. You've just got to stay here until you feel different."

The creaking died away. He stood in the center of the office, motionless. His eyes traced the coal-black course of Miss Millick's footprints to where she stood blocking the door. Then a sound that was almost a scream was wrenched out of him, for it seemed to him that the blackness was creeping up her legs under the thin stockings.

"Why, Mr Wran," she said, "You're acting as if you were crazy. You must lie down for a while. Here, I'll help you off with your coat."

The nauseously idiotic and **rasping** note was the same; only it had been intensified. As she came toward him he turned and ran through the storeroom, clattered a key desperately at the lock of the second door to the corridor.

"Why, Mr Wran," he heard her call, "are you having some kind of a fit? You must let me help you."

The door came open and he plunged out into the corridor and up the stairs immediately ahead. It was only when he reached the top that he realized the heavy steel door in front of him led to the roof. He jerked up the catch.

"Why, Mr Wran, you mustn't run away. I'm coming after you."

Then he was out on the gritty gravel of the roof. The night sky was clouded and murky, with a faint pinkish glow from the neon signs. From the distant mills rose a ghostly spurt of flame. He ran to the edge. The street lights glared dizzily upward. Two men were tiny round blobs of hat and shoulders. He swung around.

The thing was in the doorway. The voice was no longer

solicitous but moronically playful, each sentence ending in a titter.

"Why, Mr Wran, why have you come up here? We're all alone. Just think, I might push you off."

The thing came slowly toward him. He moved backward until his heels touched the low parapet. Without knowing why, or what he was going to do, he dropped to his knees. He dared not look at the face as it came nearer, a focus for the worst in the world, a gathering point for poisons from everywhere. Then the lucidity of terror took possession of his mind, and words formed on his lips.

"I will obey you. You are my god," he said. "You have supreme power over man and his animals and his machines. You rule this city and all others. I recognize that."

Again the titter, closer. "Why, Mr Wran, you never talked like this before. Do you mean it?"

"The world is yours to do with as you will, save or tear to pieces," he answered fawningly[40], his words automatically fitting themselves together in vaguely liturgical[41] patterns. "I will recognize that. I will praise, I will sacrifice. In smoke and soot I will worship you for ever."

The voice did not answer. He looked up. There was only Miss Millick, deathly pale and swaying drunkenly. Her eyes were closed. He caught her as she wobbled toward him. His knees gave way under the added weight and they sank down together on the edge of the roof.

After a while she began to twitch. Small noises came from her throat and her eyelids edged open.

"Come on, we'll go downstairs," he murmured jerkily, trying to draw her up. "You're feeling bad."

"I'm terribly dizzy," she whispered. "I must have fainted, I didn't eat enough. And then I'm so nervous lately, about the war and everything, I guess. Why, we're on the roof! Did you bring me up here to get some air? Or did I come up without

40 showing disapproval: being extremely nice to someone more important than you because you want them to like you or give you something
41 religious, like in a prayer

knowing it? I'm awfully foolish. I used to walk in my sleep, my mother said."

As he helped her down the stairs, she turned and looked at him. "Why, Mr Wran" she said, faintly, "you've got a big black smudge on your forehead. Here, let me get it off for you." Weakly she rubbed at it with her handkerchief. She started to sway again and he steadied her.

"No, I'll be all right," she said. "Only I feel cold. What happened, Mr Wran? Did I have some sort of fainting spell?"

He told her it was something like that.

Later, riding home in the empty elevated railway car, he wondered how long he would be safe from the thing. It was a purely practical problem. He had no way of knowing, but instinct told him he had satisfied the brute for some time. Would it want more when it came again? Time enough to answer that question when it arose. It might be hard, he realized, to keep out of an insane asylum[42]. With Helen and Ronny to protect, as well as himself, he would have to be careful and **tight-lipped**. He began to speculate as to how many other men and women had seen the thing or things like it.

The elevated slowed and lurched in a familiar fashion. He looked at the roofs near the curve. They seemed very ordinary, as if what made them impressive had gone away for a while.

42 *old-fashioned, now offensive:* a hospital for patients suffering from mental illnesses

Post-reading exercises

Understanding the story

1 **Use these questions to help you check that you have understood the story.**

Section 1

1 What is the relationship between Miss Millick and Mr Wran?
2 In what way is Mr Wran's behaviour different from usual?
3 How does Miss Millick react to Mr Wran's strange questions?
4 Why do you think he is talking like this?
5 How do the two of them react to the dirt on Mr Wran's desk?
6 When does the narrator stop telling the story from Miss Millick's point of view?
7 When does the story take a jump back in time? Why does it do this?
8 Why did Catesby Wran always look at the same set of rooftops every evening?
9 What did the rooftops symbolise for him?
10 What did he see on the rooftop?
11 Why did he become so obsessed with it?
12 What else did he become obsessed with?
13 Why did he decide to see a psychiatrist?
14 What did he hope the psychiatrist would say to him? Why?

Section 2

15 Why does Catesby tell the psychiatrist about his childhood?
16 What was special about him as a child?
17 How did his mother try to exploit his special abilities?
.18 What happened when the psychologists tried to test him?
19 How does Catesby feel as he tells the psychiatrist his story?
20 Why does the doctor look out of to the window?
21 What is the doctor's reaction to what he sees?
22 What does Catesby see on the window?
23 How do you think he felt as he left?
24 In what way had the doctor *taken a load off his mind*?

Section 3

25 Why does he walk around the streets rather than going home?
26 Why doesn't he switch the lights on when he goes into his office?
27 What does he remember as he sits there in the dark?
28 What other thoughts fill his mind?

29 Do you think he may be going mad? Or has he reached a new understanding of the world?
30 Why does his wife phone him?
31 Why does Catesby decide to go home?

Section 4
32 What did he see in the lift shaft?
33 How does Catesby feel as he hides in his office?
34 What does he think is going to happen?
35 How does he feel when Miss Millick walks in?
36 What does he notice about her shoes? What does he notice about the way she opens her bag?
37 Why does he run away?
38 What happens to Miss Millick on the roof? Do you think Miss Millick is possessed or is Catesby going mad?
39 How did Catesby feel as he travelled home on the elevated railway?
40 What are his fears for the future?
41 What do *you* think will happen next?

Language study

Speculating – modal verbs

At various points during the story Catesby Wran stops to speculate[43] about the nature of the ghost and its intentions. Miss Millick also speculates about her boss, the sudden change in his character and what it might mean.

They use a range of modal verbs, verb phrases and adverbs to make their speculations.

We can use the modal verbs *would, could, might* and *must* to discuss various possibilities and probabilities when speculating.

Form

We can use the modal verbs with:
(a) an infinitive: *It would be very grimy*
(b) *be + -ing*: *Miss Millick wondered if he mightn't be seeking some sort of sympathy*
(c) *have + past participle*: *which could hardly have happened*

---

43 consider or discuss why something has happened or what will happen next

Use

1 Look at the extracts in the box below; then, decide in which extract the speaker is:

1 very sure that what they say is true
2 asking for an opinion
3 giving an opinion about an imaginary situation
4 asking what possibilities exist
5 putting forward a suggestion that they are not very sure about
6 saying that something is impossible
7 putting forward a logical explanation for what happened

> (a) *of course, he **might** be joking, but it didn't sound that way*
> (b) *have you ever thought what a ghost **would** look like?*
> (c) *it **would** be very grimy*
> (d) *which **could hardly** have happened if it were at all heavy*
> (e) *you **must** be sick*
> (f) *I **must** have frightened him*
> (g) *What **could** you do to stop it from troubling you?*

2 Match the modal verbs to their meaning:

| could couldn't might must |

100% sure

.... completely sure that something is true

.... confident of an opinion about an imaginary situation

.... saying that something is a possibility, but not a certainty

.... saying that something is completely impossible

impossible

3 Rewrite the sentences below using one of the modal verbs.

She was sure there was something wrong.
'There _____,' *she said.*

It was completely impossible for him to get there on time.
He _____ *on time.*

There's a possibility that it'll rain this afternoon.
It _____ *this afternoon.*

He thought the party was going to be a disaster.
He thought the party _____ *a disaster.*

Common expressions of uncertainty

4 Look at these other examples and underline the expression used to show that the speaker is speculating.

1 *It seemed to have been blown against a rusty ventilator by the wind.*
2 *It didn't seem to have any brown in it.*
3 *Perhaps it was filled with leaves.*
4 *You look sick.*

Form

Seem

We use can use *seem* with:
(a) an adjective: *he seemed* troubled by something
(b) an infinitive: *he seemed* to be looking for something, he *seemed* to have forgotten about his patient

Look

We can use *look* with:
(a) an adjective: *he looked worried*
(b) *as if* + clause: *he looked as if he was in pain*
(c) *like* + noun phrase: *he looked like a reasonable person*

5 Use the words in brackets to make the statements below into speculations.

> For example:
> Catesby Wran was imagining things (*seem*)
> *Catesby Wran seemed to be imagining things.*

1 Miss Millick was in love with Catesby. (*maybe*)

2 The psychiatrist was a good man. (*look*)

3 He was scared by the face in the window. (*seem*)

4 The ghost would leave him alone now. (*perhaps*)

5 The rooftops were normal now and didn't frighten him anymore. (*look*)

Ellipsis

Ellipsis is a common feature of spoken English. Normally, a complete sentence must contain both a subject and a verb:

For example: **It would grow** *out of the real world.*

But sometimes, in speech, words are omitted at the beginning of a sentence, if the meaning is still clear. Notice how the second sentence below has no subject or verb. This is an example of ellipsis.

It would reflect the tangled, sordid, vicious things. All the loose ends.

6 Look at the example again. What words are missing from the beginning of the second sentence?

7 The same thing can happen with questions. Look at the example below. What words have been omitted in the second, third and fourth questions?

What would such a thing want from a person, Miss Millick? Sacrifice? Worship? Or just fear? What could you do to stop it from troubling you?

The writer uses this feature in both reported speech and when he is reporting Catesby's thoughts to create the feeling of natural speech and thought patterns.

The writer also uses a form of ellipsis when he writes non-standard, incomplete sentences, made up of a list of noun phrases. Look at this example, when Catesby is trying to describe the nature of the ghost that is haunting him:

Just picture it. A smoky composite face with the hungry anxiety of the unemployed, the neurotic restlessness of the person without purpose, the jerky tension of the high-pressure metropolitan worker, the uneasy resentment of the striker, the callous opportunism of the scab, the aggressive whine of the panhandler, the inhibited terror of the bombed civilian, and a thousand other twisted emotional patterns.

The result is that, as we read, we picture a series of different images. This builds momentum and pace. The verbs are not relevant. It is the abstract nouns, the emotions, and the faces of the people that go with them that are important.

8 **Look at the extracts below. Cross out any words that can be omitted.**

1 *But it would begin to influence your actions. It would make you do this. It would stop you from doing that.* [page 122]

2 *It's a neurosis. It must be. I must be suffering from compulsions. I must be experiencing hallucinations.* [page 124]

3 *Do you notice any more definite physical symptoms? Do you feel any pain? Do you have a headache? Do you suffer from indigestion?* [page 128]

4 *He was reliving it now. He could remember the darkened rooms. He could see the earnest assemblages of gawking, prying adults. He could picture himself, alone on a little platform, lost in a straight-backed wooden chair.* (page 129)

5 *He dared not look at the face as it came nearer, it was a focus for the worst in the world, it constituted a gathering point for poisons everywhere.* [page 137]

Literary analysis

Plot

1 Here are some of the events in the story. They are in chronological order (the order in which they happened). In what order are they described in the story? Why is the order different?

> Catesby is visited by a team of university psychologists.
> Catesby sees a strange object on a rooftop.
> Catesby visits a psychiatrist.
> The psychiatrist sees a prowler.
> Catesby's son is frightened by a face at his window.
> Catesby's secretary faints on the rooftop of their office building.

2 Look at the list of events again. Can you add any more key events? Which, do you think, is the most important event in the story? Write a one-sentence description of that event.

3 Catesby is worried that he may be going mad. What evidence is there in the story that suggests that what he sees is real? Who else has seen the ghost? Do you think that Catesby is really being haunted by some kind of urban ghost?

4 Traditional ghost stories often end with some sort of final ending, with the ghost finally finding peace, for example, or the main character being saved from some sort of danger. But there is no final ending at the end of this story. Do you think this is a strength or a weakness? Why?

Character

5 What do you know about the main character, Catesby? How is he representative of the world he lives in? Do you sympathise with him – like or care about him, feel his emotions as you read? Why/why not?

6 Do you think Catesby is suffering from hallucinations (seeing things that don't really exist)? Or is he able to see ghosts?

7 Think about the character of Miss Millick. What do you know about her? In what way is she different from Catesby? What do we learn about Catesby's character through her?

8 What do we know about the ghost? Is it real? Can everybody see it? What does it want? What does it tell us about the world at that time, the world as it is described in the story? What emotions does it arouse in the people who see it? Why is it so terrifying?

Narration

9 The story is told in the third person, but the narrator is not an all-seeing narrator. He tells the story from the point of view of his characters. Whose point of view is being used in the first section? Why? How does this help guide us in to the story?

10 When does the point of view change to Catesby? What is the advantage of continuing the story from his point of view?

11 The story starts in the middle. Why? How would it have been different if the writer had started with the first appearance of the ghost?

12 There are two flashbacks (when the main character, Catesby, looks back a) at an earlier time in his life, and b) to earlier that winter). What is Catesby remembering? What is the advantage of using a flashback?

13 The writer leaves the story open-ended. Why do you think he does this? How do you think the story should continue? Will the ghost reappear? Will Catesby be sent to an insane asylum (a hospital for people who are mentally ill)?

Atmosphere

14 What creates the atmosphere of the story? Think of the colours, sounds, smells and textures described in the story. Think of the season, the time of day and the weather. How do these add to the atmosphere? Choose three adjectives to describe the atmosphere.

15 Think of the ghost. In what way is it a product of the city and its atmosphere? What is it made of? Think about where Catesby sees it, how it moves, its colour.

Style

16 Look at the passage where Catesby first describes the rooftops where he first saw the ghost. [page 124]

Notice the adjectives he uses: *dingy, melancholy, abandoned, washed-out, drab, dirty, windblown, bleak, ugly, dreary.* What is similar about these adjectives – what do they have in common? What is the overall effect of the description?

Notice also the metaphors he uses: *a particular little* **sea** *of roofs, a dingy, melancholy little* **world** *of tar-paper.* What is the effect created by these metaphors?

Notice how Catesby contrasts adjectives to add to the mystery of the place he is describing: *bleak and suggestive; dreary, but meaningful.*

Look at the following sentences, where he explains exactly what the place – and the ghost – represent. Make a note of the adjectives he uses. Why is it significant that he only sees this spot in the 'half darkness' at the end of his working day?

17 Look at the passage where Catesby explains his reaction to the last sighting of the ghost on the rooftop. (*Afterwards he realized he must have given a muffled cry ...*) [page 126]. Read the whole paragraph and notice how the focus moves from the outside world, the people on the train, to Catesby's inner thoughts and reactions. Imagine you were one of the people on the carriage sitting near Catesby. What would you have seen? What would you have thought of this man and his strange behaviour?

Notice the structure of the sentences. The opening sentences are well-constructed, using linking words and complex clauses. But slowly the sentence structure starts to break down. What is the effect created by the series of broken clauses towards the end of the paragraph?

Is the horror real or is it in Catesby's head? How does the writer help us share the urgency and terror of Catesby's thoughts?

18 Look at the two closing paragraphs. Notice the adjectives the writer uses. How are they different from the adjectives he used when he first described the rooftops where Catesby first saw the ghost? What effect is created in these last two paragraphs? What do they show about Catesby's state of mind at the end of the story?

Guidance to the above literary terms, answer keys to all the exercises and activities, plus a wealth of other reading-practice material, can be found on the student's section of the Macmillan Readers website at: www.macmillanenglish.com/readers.

A *Spot of Gothic*

by Jane Gardam

About the author

Jane Gardam is a writer of short stories and novels for adults and children. She has won many national and international literary awards for her work. Some people have compared her to Jane Austen because she writes about the detailed day-to-day life of small, closed communities, and about women's roles within those communities. Feminists have accused her of being a conservative; conservatives have accused her of being a feminist.

Jane Gardam started writing when she was in her 30s; she is now in her 80s, and is still writing. Her earlier works focused on childhood and growing up, while her later works have focused more on growing old. She has also shown an increasing interest in the supernatural in her later works, in particular the short-story collections *Going into a Dark House* (1994), *Missing the Midnight: Hauntings and Grotesques* (1997) and her novel, *The Queen of the Tambourine* (1991) – the haunting story of a woman's fascination with a mysterious stranger.

Gardam was born in Yorkshire in 1928 and spent her childhood there. She left Yorkshire when she finished school, and won a scholarship to study English at Bedford College in London. After finishing her degree, she worked as a travelling librarian with the Red Cross in London, before joining the editorial staff of a literary magazine.

She left her job with the magazine when her first child was born, and started writing her first novel on the day her third child started school. *A Few Fair Days*, published in 1971, was set in Yorkshire and told the story of a young girl growing up in the 1930s. Her first adult novel, *God on the Rocks* (1978), was also a story about growing up. It was nominated for the Booker Prize[1] and was later adapted for television.

Gardam has had a long and successful writing career. She has written 28 books, including novels and short-story collections, and in 1999, she was awarded the Heywood Hill Literary Prize[2] in recognition

1 also known as the Man Booker Prize, a literary award given each year to the best original full-length novel, written in the English language, by a citizen of either the Commonwealth of Nations or the Republic of Ireland

2 annual award given to a writer, editor, reviewer, collector or publisher for a lifelong contribution to the enjoyment of books

of a distinguished literary career. Her latest novel, *Old Filth*, the story of a retired lawyer from Hong Kong, was shortlisted for the Orange Prize[3] in 2005.

She continues to write reviews for *The Spectator* and *The Telegraph*, as well as for BBC radio. Her latest book is *The People on Privilege Hill* (2007), a collection of short stories.

About the story

A Spot of Gothic was first published in 1980 in *The Sidmouth Letters*, a collection of 11 of her short stories. It is the only story in the collection which deals with the supernatural. It is set in a remote corner of Yorkshire in autumn 1980.

Background information

Gothic literature

The term 'Gothic literature' refers to dark, frightening and mysterious stories. Gothic literature has terror and the supernatural as its main theme. Its tales are set in remote, rural locations, where ruined churches, castles and stately homes hide in deep, dark forests. Its stories describe death and madness. Its characters are romantic and prone to melancholy (sadness).

Yorkshire Dales

All the place names in the story refer to small towns and villages in the Yorkshire Dales, the hills in North West Yorkshire in the north of England, or to farmhouses and properties in the area. The area described is remote and rural. There are very few villages, the country roads are small and often full of sheep or other farm animals. Only a few people live there, most of them are farmers. The Northern Dales, or the fells as they are referred to in the story, are highlands, with very little vegetation or trees, except those planted around houses to give them shelter from the cold winds. The people who live there have a reputation for being suspicious of outsiders.

Catterick military base

The Catterick Garrison is a large military base in the north of Yorkshire. Currently, it is home to more than 18,000 people. Many families

---

3 annual international award for the best full-length novel, written in English, by a woman

choose to live on the base, but others choose to find accommodation in the local area.

Summary

It may help you to know something about what happens in the story before you read it. Don't worry, this summary does not tell you how the story ends.

A young soldier's wife is left on her own in a remote rural area of North Yorkshire when her husband is sent to Hong Kong. At first she is worried that she will be lonely. Her husband has told her that the people in the area are closed and cold, but she soon finds that they are, in fact, very warm and welcoming. They bring her beans from their garden and invite her into their homes.

She is invited to dinner at an old stately home[4], 'Mealbeck', by two elderly sisters who live there. After dinner, when she is driving home along the empty country road, she sees a woman waving to her from her garden. She keeps driving, but something about the figure scares her.

She stops her car and wonders whether she should go back, but she doesn't think the woman needed help. It seemed rather, that she recognised her and was waving to her.

She tells a neighbour about her experience. She wonders if she's seen a ghost, but her neighbour pays little attention to her story. So she drives back to the house in daylight. She finds the house and sits at the gate, wondering if she should go in, when she feels a presence behind her. She turns round and sees the same woman she saw the night before. The woman asks her the time, and then walks away.

As she is leaving, she meets the doctor coming to make a house call. She tells him about the woman. He tells her that she, too, is a soldier's wife, living on her own.

Later, when she arrives home, her neighbour tells her that the woman she saw has committed suicide[5]. At a second dinner party at the home of the same two elderly sisters, the guests talk about the woman and her sad story.

---

4 a large house in the UK that has an interesting history and belongs, or used to belong, to an important family
5 (vb) to deliberately killing yourself

Pre-reading exercises

Key vocabulary

This section will help you familiarise yourself with some of the more specific vocabulary used in the story. You may want to use it to help you before you start reading, or as a revision exercise after you have finished the story.

Local accent and dialect

The author often writes the characters' words as they would say them, changing the standard spelling to show their accent. Here are some of the features of a Yorkshire accent, which should help you to better understand the dialogue in the story:

1 The definite article (*the*) is often dropped or reduced to the letter 't': '*It's the bill fort telephone.*' (for **the** telephone)

2 The initial 'h' of a word is often silent: *So 'e's off then?* (**he**'s off/ going?); *'ere* (**here**). Note: 'then' at the end of the sentence often reinforces a question. For example, *So 'e's off **then**?* has the same meaning as 'So, is he going?' or 'He's going, is he?' – in these cases, 'then' does *not* mean 'afterwards' or 'next'.

3 The final 'g' is dropped in –*ing* forms: *You'll be missin' the Captain.* (missin**g**)

4 Other contractions: *wi'* instead of '**with**'; *Y'd* instead of '**you**'d'

5 Some pronouns change: 'you' becomes *yer*; 'my' becomes *me*; 'himself' becomes *hisself*.

6 The long vowel sounds are often shortened. For example, 'been' becomes *bin*; 'maybe' becomes *mebbe*.

1 Look at these extracts. Rewrite them in standard English.

1 *They're growin out of me ears.*

_____

2 *Come rount back but wear yer wellies[6].*

_____

3 *Comin over for yer tea then?*

_____

4 *Y'd get a fair plateful there.*

_____

6 rubber boots that are worn in mud and wet conditions

5 *When they can spare't time.*

6 *Did yer stop?*

7 *I hear yer've bin gallivanting⁷ at the Hall.*

2 There are also some words that are characteristic of the north of England. Look at these extracts. What do you think the words in bold mean?

1 *It's me sister's birthday tomorrow. I **near** forgot.*
2 *She hasn't had them curtains down in a **twelve-month**.*
3 *'ello there, Mrs Bainbridge, now. **Grand** day.*
4 *There's **nowt** amiss⁸ wi' them.*
5 *Did you have a **fair** drive home?*
6 *I saw a ghost. Oh **aye**, y'd see half a dozen after a night out at Mealbeck.*

3 Compare your answers with the words in the box.

> almost   beautiful   good   nothing   year   yes

Describing the Dales

The story is set against the background of the simple, **no-nonsense, down-to-earth** sheep-farming community of the Yorkshire Dales. Understanding the landscape and the geography of the Dales is important in understanding the main themes of the story.

4 Look at the extracts a–d from the story, below. Match the words in bold with the definitions below.

> (a) *I suddenly saw a woman at her cottage gate, waving at me gently like an old friend. In a lonely (1) **dale** this is not very surprising, as I had found out. Several times I have met someone at a (2) **lane** end flapping a letter that has missed the post in Kirby Thore or Hawes.*

> (b) *Language addressed to animals was foul and unrefined, ringing over the fells and (3) **sheep dips** and (4) **clipping sheds** – but bore no relation to conversation with humans or at any rate not with me.*

7 at a party
8 wrong

(c) *The road had dropped low to a (5)* **humped bridge**, *and after a moment when I had switched off the engine I could hear the clear quick brown water running deep and noisy below it … I got out of the car and walked about. It was cold. I stood on the bridge. Apart from the noise of the (6)* **beck** *everything was absolutely quiet.*

(d) *The (7)* **fell** *that had looked so bare at night, by daylight could be seen to be dotted with crumpled, (8)* **squat** *little stone farms, their backs turned to the view, two trees to each to form a wind-break.*

(a) a small stream
(b) the buildings where farmers cut the wool from the sheep
(c) an old word meaning 'valley', now mainly used to talk about valleys in the north of England
(d) a hill, or area of high land, especially in the north of England
(e) a small, steep, curved bridge
(f) a narrow road, especially in the countryside
(g) a bath of liquid chemical used for killing insects in a sheep's skin
(h) low, built to be sheltered from the wind

Describing the houses

The houses described in the story add to the gothic atmosphere, with dark, **overgrown** gardens – plants growing high and thick and not being cut back, stone walls and floors, and a feeling of old, decaying (slowly dying) grandeur (wealth and luxury).

5 **Read the dictionary definitions below. Then complete the descriptions of two of the houses in the story using the words in the definitions.**

dahlias noun [a] large brightly coloured flowers that are grown in gardens
flagged adj covered with flat pieces of stone
gravel noun [U] small pieces of stone that are used to make paths and roads
ha-ha noun [C] a type of wall or boundary to a garden that is built inside a hole, so that it is invisible and doesn't interrupt the view of the surrounding countryside.
hedge noun [C] a line of bushes or small trees
honeysuckle noun [C] a climbing plant with yellow or pink flowers
mill a building where grain is made into flour
yew noun [C] a tree with dark green leaves that produce a bright red fruit

The house he had found was beautiful, old and tall in an old garden, on the edge of a village on the edge of the fell. It was comfortable and dark with a (1) .... floor and old furniture. Roses and (2) .... were nearly strangling black (3) .... of neglected (4) ....

A woman in the ironmonger's buying paraffin in gloves and hat invited me to tea in a farmhouse the size of a (5) .... with a (6) .... and a terrace at the back, (7) .... a foot thick and a thousand (8) .... staked liked artillery men and luminous with autumn.

Main themes

Before you read the story, you may want to think about some of its main themes. The questions will help you think about the story as you're reading it for the first time. There is more discussion of the main themes in the *Literary analysis* section after the story.

Small communities

The story takes place in a small, rural community. One of the themes of the story is the potential isolation and loneliness that people can experience when they live in a small community. But, at the same time, it also describes the positive features of life in a small community.

6 As you read the story, notice how the people and places are described and ask yourself:

– In what way are they different from the storyteller's expectation?

Ghostly warnings

In many ghost stories, the ghost has a message to give the person who sees it. The message is often a warning. In some stories, the ghost can only rest when it has saved someone from an accident, or from making the same mistake the ghost had made in its own life.

7 As you read the story, think about the figure of the woman in the garden:

– What had happened to her?
– What message might she have to give the storyteller?
– How does the encounter with the ghost change the storyteller's life?

Gothic atmosphere

The title of the story suggests that it is a tribute to Gothic literature, and suggests that it will explore the same themes. Gothic horror stories are often set in isolated, but beautiful, settings. They combine beauty with fear, and a fascination with past times and the world of the supernatural. As you read the story, consider to what extent this story is a Gothic story.

A *Spot of Gothic*

by Jane Gardam

I was **whizzing** along the road out of Wensleydale through Low Thwaite beyond Naresby when I suddenly saw a woman at her cottage gate, waving at me gently like an old friend. In a lonely dale this is not very surprising, as I had found out. Several times I have met someone at a lane end **flapping** a letter that has missed the post in Kirby Thore or Hawes. "It's me sister's birthday tomorrow. I near forgot" or "It's the bill fort telephone. We'll **be cut off** next thing." The curious thing about this figure, so still and watchful, was that it was standing there waving to me in the middle of the night.

It was full moon. I had been out to dinner at Mealbeck. I had only been living in the North for two months and for one month alone. I had joined my husband near Catterick camp the minute he had found us a house, which was only a few days before he found that the regiment was being posted to Hong Kong. The house he had found was beautiful, old and tall in an old garden, on the edge of a village on the edge of the fell. It was comfortable and dark with a flagged floor and old furniture. Roses and honeysuckle were nearly strangling black hedges of **neglected** yew. There was nice work to be done

It was the best army house we had ever found. The posting to Hong Kong promised to be a short one. I had been there before and hated it – I hate crowded places – and I decided to stay behind alone.

He said, "But you will be alone, mind. The camp is a good way off and most people will have gone with us. It's the North. You'll make no friends. They take ten years to do more than **wag** their heads at you in the street up here. Now, are you sure?"

I said I was and I stayed and found that he was quite wrong. Within days, almost within hours of my miserable drive home from Darlington Station to **see him off**, I found that I was behaving as if I'd always known the people here and they were doing the same to me. I got home from the station and stopped the car outside my beautiful front door and sat still, thinking, "He has gone again. Again he has gone. What a marriage. Always alone. Shall I forget his face again? Like last time? Shall I begin to **brood**? Over-eat? Drink by myself in the evenings – rather more every evening? Shall I start tramping about the lanes pretending I like long walks?" I sat there thinking and a great truculent[9] female head with glaring eyes stuck itself through the car window.

"D'you want some *beans?*"

"Oh!"

"Some *beans?* Stick beans[10]?"

"Oh I don't – ? Can you spare – ?"

"Beans, beans. Masses of beans. They're growin' out of me ears. Grand beans. Up to you."

"I'd love some beans."

A sheaf[11] of them was dumped on the seat beside me. "There's plenty more. You've just to say so. So 'e's off then? The Captain?"

"Yes."

"Well, yer not to fret. There's always a cup of tea at our place. Come rount back but wear yer wellies or you'll get in a slather[12] int yard."

In the post office they asked kindly for news. Of how I was settling, of where I had come from. The vicar called. A man in a land-rover with a kind face – the doctor – waved his hat. A woman in the ironmonger's buying paraffin in gloves and hat invited me to tea in a farmhouse the size of a mill with a ha-ha and a terrace at the back, gravel a foot thick and a thousand dahlias staked like artillerymen and luminous with autumn. The tea cups must have been two hundred years old.

9 *formal, old-fashioned:* easily annoyed and always ready to argue or fight
10 green beans which are grown on plants that are supported by long wooden sticks
11 usually stems of grain which have been cut and tied together
12 *old-fashioned:* a sticky mess

I was asked to small places too – a farm so isolated that the sheep and cows looked up aghast[13] when I found my way to it, and the sheep-dogs nearly garrotted[14] themselves on the end of hairy ropes.

"You'll be missin the Captain," the farmer's wife said as she opened the door. Her accent was not the local one.

I said, "You talk differently," and she said, "Well, I would do. I come from Stennersceugh. It was a Danish settlement long since. It's all of ten miles off."

Never in my life had I had so much attention paid to me by strangers, nor been told so many intimate things from the heart – of marriages, love and death; of children or the lack of them, fears of sickness, pregnancy; of lost loves and desperate remedies. Three old ladies living by the church, I heard, drank three crates[15] of sherry a week ("It's the chemist delivers"). A husband had "drowned 'isself in Ash Beck for fear of a thing growing out of the side of his head".

There seemed to be total classlessness[16], total acceptance, offence only taken if you **gave yourself airs**[17], offered money in return for presents or didn't open your door wide enough at the sound of every bell. There was a certain amount of derision at bad management – "She never gets out to the shops till twelve o'clock." "She hasn't had them curtains down in a twelve-month" – but I met no violence, no hatred. There were threats of "bringin me gun" to walkers on the fells with unleashed dogs, but not one farmer in ten possessed a gun or would have known how to use it if he had. Language addressed to animals was foul[18] and unrefined[19], ringing over the fells and sheep dips and clipping sheds – but bore no relation to conversation with humans or at any rate not with me. "Come ere yer bloody, buggerin little

13 shocked and upset
14 garotte (vb) – kill someone by pulling something very tight around their neck
15 a box which is divided into individual sections and used to carry bottles
16 not divided into social classes
17 to put on/give yourself airs (vb) – behaviour that is not natural and relaxed, by someone who wants to impress someone and seem important
18 dirty, unpleasant
19 *formal*: not polite, shows a lack of education or good manners

– 'ello there, Mrs Bainbridge, now. Grand day. Comin over for yer tea then?"

Alan had told me that when he came home I'd be used to my tea[20] as my supper and then more tea just before bedtime and I would forget how to cook a steak. However he was wrong again, because it had been dinner I had been invited to at Mealbeck the night of the waving woman, and a much better dinner than I'd ever have got in Aldershot[21].

Mealbeck is the big Gothic house of two sisters – a magnificent cold, turreted, slightly idiotic house, something between the Brighton Pavilion[22] and the Carpathians[23]. We ate not in a corner of it but the corner of a corner, passing from the **tremendous** door, over flagged[24] halls, a great polar-bear skin rug and down a long cold passage. At the end was a little room which must once have been the housekeeper's and **crammed** into it among the housekeeper's possessions – a clock, a set of bells, a little hat-stand, a photograph of servants like rows of suet dumplings[25], starched and stalwart[26] and long ago dead – were a Thomas Lawrence[27], photographs by Lenare[28] and haunted Ypres[29] faces in 1914 khaki[30]. On the housekeeper's old table where she must have handed out the wages were some fine silver and glasses fit for emperors.

Good wine, too. The sisters, Millicent and Gertie, knew their wine. They also knew their scotch and resorted to it wordlessly after the best pheasant and lemon pudding I think I've ever eaten.

20 *colloquial:* the evening meal, usually referred to as *dinner* or *supper*, is often referred to as *tea* in some parts of the country, particularly the north of England
21 a town with an army base in the south of England
22 a 19th-century palace built in a very luxurious Indian style
23 the mountain range between Poland and Rumania, associated with Gothic tales such as Count Dracula
24 the floor is covered in flagstones – a hard piece of stone used for making a floor or path
25 balls of dough
26 loyal, strong
27 Thomas Lawrence was a classic English 19th-century portrait artist
28 early 20th-century French society photographer
29 a town in Belgium that was the centre of intense battles during the First World War
30 the colour of army uniforms in the First World War

I said, "Oh this has been lovely. Lovely." We stood under the green moon that did not so much light the fells as isolate them in the long clean lines of the faded day.

"You are from Sussex," said Millicent. "You must find this very bare."

"It's wonderful. I love it."

"I hope you'll stay the winter," said Gertie. "And I hope you'll come here soon again."

The two of them walked, not too steadily to the iron gates and I roared off in the little Fiat down the drive and out on to the fell, between the knobbly[31] blocks of stone walls flashing up in the car lights. I felt **minute** between the long lines snaking away, the long low undecorated horizon, the clear hard pencil lines cut with a very sharp hard point. Gigantic lamp-eyes of sheep now and then came shining into the headlights. It was midnight. I did not meet a single car between Mealbeck and Naresby and the road ripped up and down, narrow and sweeping and black and quiet. I thought of Alan in Hong Kong. It would be breakfast time. I wished he were with me. Then I forgot him in the emptiness of the road under the moon and the great encircling ball of the stars.

I went flying through High Thwaite, **hurtling** through Low Thwaite and the same landscape spread out still in front of me – endlessly deserted, not a light in any cottage, not a dog barking, not a cry of a bird. It was just after what appeared to be the loneliest part of the road that I took a corner rather faster than I should and saw the woman standing in her garden and waving at me with a slow decorous[32] arm, a queenly arm. You could see from the moonlight that her head was piled up high with queenly hair. I think I was about two miles on before I really **took it in**. I was so shaken by it that I stopped the car.

I was not many miles from home now – my village, my new house, my heavy safe front door. The road had dropped low to a humped bridge, and after a moment when I had switched off the engine I could hear the clear quick brown water running deep

31 covered with small, hard bumps; rarely used, usually now to describe knees
32 *formal*: polite and formal

and noisy below it. I thought, "There can't have been anyone. I'm drunk."

I got out of the car and walked about. It was cold. I stood on the bridge. Apart from the noise of the beck everything was absolutely quiet. There was not a light from any house in any direction. Down here by the beck I could see no horizon, not the fell's edge, not even the sweet nibbled grass beside the road. The air smelled very clean like fresh sheets.

This was the pedlars'[33] road. For five hundred years, they had walked it with packs of ribbons and laces and buttons and medicines, and a great many of them according to all the stories had been murdered for them or disappeared in the snow in winter – often not found until Martinmas[34]. If my car doesn't start now, I thought, I shall be very much alone.

Had the woman been asking for help? I wondered whether to go back. I felt absolutely certain – and it is amazing how much even at midnight under only the palest moon the eye can know from the angle of a moving arm – that she hadn't.

She had been waving kindly. Not afraid. Not asking. Not even **beckoning**. She had been waving in some sort of recognition.

I had never been so **frightened in my life**.

———

"I went to Mealbeck last night."

"Y'd get a fair plateful[35] there."

"Yes."

"And a fair skinful[36]."

"We – yes. Lovely wine."

"Wine, eh? And mebbe a tot[37]?"

"I had a lovely time. They're very nice. Very kind."

"That's right. They're kind. Home boozers[38]. Did you get back safe? They say the police sits outside Mealbeck when there's entertaining. When they can spare't time."

33 someone who goes from place to place selling things
34 November 11th, St Martin's Day
35 *dialect*: a good meal
36 *informal*: a large amount of alcohol
37 a measure of whisky; in Scotland known as a 'dram'
38 *informal*: people who enjoy drinking alcohol

"I'm not saying anything against them."

"That's right then." He – it was the farmer who had the demented dogs and whose wife came from the Danish settlement – he looked satisfied. I could see he had been wondering if I was too fancy to answer back. "They're right. Old Gertie and Millicent. There's nowt amiss wi' them. Did you have a fair drive home?"

"Fair," I said. "One thing wasn't though. I passed a place— . I saw a ghost."

"Oh aye. Y'd see half a dozen after a night out at Mealbeck."

"No, I don't think it was that. I saw someone at a gate. It was a woman waving."

"Oh aye."

"Well – it was nearly one o'clock in the morning."

"Did yer stop?" He was clipping[39]. The sheep was taut between his legs, its yellow eyes glaring. The clippers snapped deep into the dirty heathery wool.

"Well, no. I didn't believe it till I was miles past. It took a minute. Then I thought I'd dreamed. Dropped asleep."

"Woman was it? Dark haired?"

"I didn't see the colour. Just the shape."

"Did yer go back?"

"No – well. She didn't seem to be in trouble or anything. I hope I did right. Not going back."

He said nothing till the fleece of the sheep fell away and the animal sprang out of his clutches like a soul released and slithered dizzily light in the yard.

"Watch now or yer'll get yerself hiked[40]," he said as I stood clear. "The Missus'll have a pot of tea if you fancy it."

"*Was* it a ghost?"

"Missus!"

She appeared at the door and looked pleased to see me – this really was a wonderfully friendly country – "Kettle's on," she called. "I hear yer've bin gallivanting at the Hall."

"Was it a ghost?" I asked again before I went into tea.

39 cutting the wool from a sheep
40 *dialect:* caught on the sheep's horns

"I'd not think so," he said.

———

I went back along the road the very next day and at first I could find no sign of the house at all. Or at any rate I could not decide which one it was. The fell that had looked so bare at night, by daylight could be seen to be dotted with crumpled, squat little stone farms, their backs turned to the view, two trees to each to form a wind-break, grey with white stone slabs to the window and only a tall spire of smoke to show they were occupied. It was not the townsfolk-country-cottage belt[41] so that there was not much white paint about, lined curtains, urns on yard walls – and any one of several little isolated farms could have been the eerie one. In the end I turned back and found the bridge where I'd stopped. I got out of the car again as I had before, and walked back a mile or two until I came to a lane going alongside a garden end. All I could see from the road was the garden end – a stone wall and a gate quite high up above me and behind that a huge slab-stoned roof so low that the farmhouse must have been built deep down in a dip.

Now nobody stood at the gate – more of a look-out post, a signalling post above the road. There were tangled flowers behind it. There was no excuse for me to go up the lane that must have led to the house and it was not inviting. I thought of pretending to have lost my way or asking for a drink of water but these things you grow out of doing. I might perhaps just ask if there were eggs for sale. This was quite usual. Yet I **hung back** because the lane was dark and overgrown. I sat down instead on a **rickety** milk platform meant for churns but all stuck through with nettles and which hardly took my weight. It must have been years since any churn was near it. I sat there in the still afternoon and nobody passed.

Then I felt I was being watched. There was no sound of snapping twig, no breathing and no branch stirred but I looked quickly up and into a big bewildered face, mouth a little open, large bright mooning eyes. The hair was waved deeply like an

41 the area where people from the towns buy country cottages to spend their holidays and weekends in

old *Vogue* photograph and the neckline of the dress was rounded, quite high with a string of pearls. The hands of the woman were on the wall and I think they were gloved – neat pretty kid[42] gloves. The trappings of the whole figure were all **the very soul of** order and confidence. The figure itself, however, almost yearned with uncertainty and loss.

"Whatever *time* is it?" she said.

"About three o'clock." I found I had stood up and turned to face her. For all the misery in the face there were the relics of unswervable[43] good manners which demanded good manners back; as well as a quite curious sensation, quite without visible foundation, that this body, this dotty[44] half-bemused memsahib[45] had once commanded respect, inspired good sense.

"It's just after three," I said again.

"Oh, good *gracious* – good gracious[46]." She turned with a funny, bent movement feeling for the wall to support her as she moved away. The face had not been an old woman's but the stance, the **tottering** walk were ancient. The dreadful sense of loss, the melancholy, were so thick in the air that there was almost a smell, a sick smell of them.

She was gone, and utterly silently, as if I had slept for a moment in the sunshine and had a momentary dream. She had seemed like a shade, a classical Greek shade, though why I should think of ancient Greece in bleak North Westmorland I did not know.

As I stood looking up at the gate there was a muffled[47] urgent plunging noise and round the bend of the road came sheep – a hundred of them with a shepherd and two dogs. The sheep shouldered each other, **fussing**, pushing, a stream of fat fleeces pressed together, eyes sharp with pandemonium. The dogs were happily tearing about. The shepherd walked with long steps behind. The sheep new-clipped filled the road like snow. They stopped when they saw me, then when they were **yelled** at came

42 leather made from a young goat's skin
43 which cannot be changed or shaken
44 *informal, old-fashioned*: slightly confused, not completely sane
45 Indian English, an old word used to refer to a European woman
46 *old-fashioned*: used for expressing surprise
47 not easy to hear, sound that is blocked or stifled

on **careering** drunkenly round me, surrounding me and I stood knee deep in them and the flat blank rattle of bleats[48], the smell of sheep dip and dog and man – and petrol, for when I looked beyond I found a land-rover had been crawling behind and at the wheel the doctor with the tweed hat was sitting laughing.

He said, "Well! You look terrified."

"They were so sudden."

"They'll not hurt you."

"No. I know – just they were so – quiet. They broke in –"

"Broke in?"

"To the silence. It's very – silent here, isn't it?" I was inane.

He got down from the car and came round near me. "You've not been here long, have you? We haven't been introduced. I'm the doctor."

"I know. I'm – "

"Yes, I know too. And we're to know each other better. We're both to go dining out at the good sisters' in a week or so. I gather we're not supposed to know it yet. We are both supposed to be lonely."

I said how could one be lonely here? I had made friends so fast.

"Some are," he said. "Who aren't born to it. Not many. It's always all right at first." We both looked together towards the high gate and he said, 'Poor Rose. My next patient. Not that I expect to be let in."

"Is she–?"

"A daughter of the regiment like yourself. Well, I mustn't discuss patients. I call on her now and then."

He walked up the side lane waving the tweed hat and left me. As he reached the point where the little lane bent out of sight he turned and cheerfully waved again, and I turned too and walked the two miles back to my car. As I reached it the land-rover passed me going very fast and the doctor made no signal and I could not see his face. I thought he must be **reckless** to drive at that lick[49] on a sheep-strewn road but soon forgot it in

48 the sound that sheep make
49 *informal:* at such speed

the pleasure of the afternoon – the bright fire I'd light at home and the smell of wood smoke and supper with a book ahead. No telephone, thank God. As I turned into my yard I found I was very put out to see Mrs Metcalfe coming across it with yet another great basket of beans.

"Tek 'em or leave 'em," she said. "But we've more than we'll ever want and they'll just get the worm in. Here, you could do wi' a few taties[50] too from the look of you. Oh aye – and I've just heard. That daft woman up near Mealbeck. She's dead. The doctor's just left her. Or I hear tell. She hanged herself."

――――

It was no story.

Or rather it is the most detestable, inadmissible story. For I don't yet know half the facts and I don't feel I want to invent any. It would be a story so easy to improve upon. There are half a dozen theories about poor Rose's hanging and half a dozen about the reason for her growing isolation and idleness and seclusion. There is only one view about her character though, and that is odd because the whole community in the fells and Dales survives on firmly-grounded assessment of motives and results; the gradations and developments of character are vital to life and give validity to passing years. Reputations change and rise and fall. But Rose – Rose had always been very well-liked and had very much liked living here. Gertie and Millicent said she had **fitted in** round here as if she were country born. She had been one of the few southerners they said who had seemed to belong. She had loved the house – a queer[51] place. It had been the heart of a Quaker[52] settlement. Panes of glass so thick you could hardly see out. She had grown more and more attached to it. She didn't seem able to leave it in the end.

"The marriage broke up after the War," said the doctor. We were sitting back after dinner in the housekeeper's room among the Thomas Lawrences. 'He was always on the move. Rose had no quarrel with him you know. She just grew – well, very taken

50 *dialect*: potatoes
51 *old-fashioned*: strange
52 a religious movement based on quiet reflection and personal beliefs

with the place. It was – yes, possession. Greek idea – possession by local gods. The Romans were here you know. They brought a Greek legend or two with them."

I said, "How odd, when I saw her I thought of the Greeks, though I hadn't known what I meant. It was the way she moved – so old. And the way she held her hands out. Like – well, sort of like on the walls of Troy."

"Not Troy," said the doctor. "More like hell, poor thing. She was quite gone[53]. You know – these fells, all the little isolated houses, I'm not sure how good for you they are, unless you're farming folk."

Millicent said rubbish.

"No," he said, "I mean it. D'you remember C. S. Lewis's[54] hell? A place where people live in isolation unable to reach each other. Where the houses get further and further apart?"

"Everyone reaches each other here," I said. "Surely?"

The doctor was looking at me and I noticed he was looking at me very hard. He said, "What was it you said?"

"Everyone reaches each other – "

"No," he said. "You said you saw her."

"Yes I did. I saw her on the way home from here, the night before she died. Then I saw her again the next day, the very afternoon. That's what is so terrible. I must have seen her, just before she – did it. I must be the last person to have seen her."

"I wonder," he said, "if that could be true." Gertie and Millicent were busy with coffee cups. They turned away.

"'Could be true? But it is certainly true. I know exactly when. She asked me the time that afternoon. I told her. It was just after three. She seemed very – bewildered about it. You called upon her hardly a quarter of an hour later. She'd hardly been back in the house a quarter of an hour."

"She'd been in it longer than that," he said, "When I found her she'd been dead for nearly three weeks. Maybe since hay-time[55]."

I went to Hong Kong.

53 *euphemism*: mad
54 an Irish writer
55 a festival celebrated in the Yorkshire Dales that runs from May to September

Post-reading exercises

Understanding the story

1 **Use these questions to help you check that you have understood the story.**

Section 1

1 Where is the story set?
2 How long has the writer been there?
3 What is her husband's attitude to her choice? Why?
4 In what ways is her husband proved wrong?
5 Does it take her long to get to know her neighbours?
6 What kind of people are they?
7 Does she feel lonely?
8 Does she miss her husband?
9 What and where is 'Mealbeck'?
10 What is special about the house?
11 How did she feel as she drove home?
12 What effect did the fell have on her?
13 Why didn't she stop when she saw the woman?
14 Why did she stop on the bridge?
15 Why did the sight of the woman frighten her so much?

Section 2

16 What was her neighbour's attitude to her story?
17 How do you think she felt after her conversation with him?

Section 3

18 Why did she go back to look for the woman?
19 Why didn't she go up to the house?
20 What struck her about the woman's appearance?
21 What kind of feelings did she associate with her?
22 Did she still think she was a ghost?
23 What interrupted her thoughts after the woman had disappeared?
24 Was she glad to see the doctor?
25 What did she learn about the woman from the doctor?
26 How did she find out about the woman's death?

Section 4

27 How did she feel about the woman's death?
28 Why did the woman kill herself?
29 When did she kill herself?
30 Why did the writer decide to go to Hong Kong?

Language study

The narrative in *A Spot of Gothic* does not follow a simple, chronological sequence. It jumps **back and forth**, and often needs to refer back to actions that have gone before.

Structuring the narrative: using the past perfect simple and continuous

Form

Past perfect simple
had ('d) + past participle
A man **had drowned** hisself.

Past perfect continuous
had + been + -ing
He **had been wondering** if I was too fancy to answer back.

Use

We use the **past perfect simple** to show that an action took place **before** a certain point in time in the past.

1 **Look at this example and answer the questions below.**

> *In the end I turned back and found the bridge where **I'd stopped**. I got out of the car again as **I had** before, and walked back a mile or two until I came to a lane.*

a) Which actions happened first?
b) When did they happen?
c) What verb form is used to talk about the main events?

We use the **past perfect continuous** to talk about an action that was happening before, or leading up to, a fixed point in the past.

2 **Look at this example and answer the questions below.**

> *She **had been waving** kindly. Not afraid. Not asking. Not even beckoning. She **had been waving** in some sort of recognition.*

a) What point in time is the storyteller referring to?
b) Why does she use the past perfect continuous and not the past perfect simple?

Stative verbs in the past perfect

We do not usually use stative verbs in the continuous. Look at the example below.

*When I **found** her she'**d been** dead for nearly three weeks.*

The sequence of the actions in this sentence is the key to the whole story.

3 **Complete these extracts using the past perfect simple or past perfect continuous of the verbs in brackets.**

1 .... the woman .... (ask) for help? I wondered whether to go back. [page 163]

2 *The fell that* .... *(look) so bare at night, by daylight could be seen to be dotted with crumpled, squat little stone farms.* [page 163]

3 *I found I* .... *(stand) up and turned to face her.* [page 164]

4 *When I looked beyond I found a land-rover* .... *(crawl) behind [the sheep] and at the wheel the doctor with the tweed hat was sitting laughing.* [page 165]

5 *Rose* .... *(always/be) very well-liked and* .... *(very much/ like) living here. Gertie and Millicent said she* .... *(fit) in round here as if she were country born.* [page 166]

6 *'You called upon her hardly a quarter of an hour later. She* .... *(hardly/be) back in the house a quarter of an hour.'*
'She .... *(be) in it longer than that,' he said.* [page 167]

Adding detail: participle clauses

The storyteller in A *Spot of Gothic* often uses participle clauses to add detail to her descriptions. There is an example in the very first sentence. The detail described in the participle clause is repeated again and again throughout the story:

*I was whizzing along the road out of Wensleydale through Low Thwaite beyond Naresby when I suddenly saw a woman **waving at me gently like an old friend.***

Form

Participle clauses are 'reduced clauses' – they contain a verb, but they do not contain a subject.

In present participle clauses we use the -ing form of the verb: *feeling for the wall*

In past participle clauses we use the past participle: *staked like artillerymen*

Present participle clauses (-ing clauses) replace verbs in the active.

Past participle clauses (-ed clauses) replace verbs in the passive.

> *She felt for the wall* → *feeling for the wall*
>
> *They had been staked like artillerymen* → *staked like artillerymen*

Use

Participle clauses are mainly used in writing. They allow the writer to condense relative clauses and combine sentences.

4 Look at these sentences. Notice how they have been combined in the extracts from the story. Notice which words have been omitted or changed.

The sheep shouldered each other. They fussed and they pushed like a stream of fat fleeces that had been pressed together.

*The sheep shouldered each other, **fussing, pushing**, a stream of fat fleeces **pressed together**.*

5 Combine the sentences below using a participle clause. We have done the first one as an example.

1 *There seemed to be total classlessness, total acceptance. Offence was only taken if you gave yourself airs. Or if you offered money in return for presents.* [page 158]

There seemed to be total classlessness, total acceptance, offence only taken if you gave yourself airs or offered money in return for presents.

---

2 *Language addressed to animals was foul and unrefined. It would ring over the fells and sheep dips and clipping sheds.* [page 158]

---

3 *I took a corner rather faster than I should and saw the woman. She was standing in her garden. She was waving at me.* [page 160]

---

4   *The sheep was taut between his legs. Its yellow eyes were glaring.*
    [page 162]

5   *The animal sprang out of his clutches. It was like a soul that had been
    released.* [page 162]

6   *As I turned into my yard I found I was very put out to see Mrs Metcalfe.
    She was coming across the yard with yet another great basket of beans.*
    [page 166]

Compare your answers to the original sentences in the story.

Multiple-clause sentences

Multiple-clause sentences are a feature of authentic written texts. They
allow the writer to include a number of details within one sentence.

6 Look at the sentence below. Divide it into six separate clauses.

*The fell that had looked so bare at night, by daylight could be seen to be
dotted with crumpled, squat little stone farms, their backs turned to the
view, two trees to each to form a wind-break, grey with white stone slabs
to the window and only a tall spire of smoke to show they were occupied.*
[page 163]

Notice how commas and the linker *and* are used to separate the clauses.

**7 Look at the sentence below. How many clauses has it got? Add
commas where necessary to divide the clauses.**

*I went flying through High Thwaite hurtling through Low Thwaite and the
same landscape spread out still in front of me – endlessly deserted not a
light in any cottage not a dog barking not a cry of a bird.* [page 160]

Literary analysis

Plot

1   Order the events in the plot according to their sequence in time.
    The writer arrived in the Yorkshire Dales   _____
    The writer left the Yorkshire Dales   _____
    The writer saw the woman in the middle of the night   _____
    She saw her again the next day   _____
    A woman killed herself   _____

The doctor visited the woman   _____
The writer met the doctor on his way to see the woman _____
The writer heard the full story of the woman's death   _____

2 In what way is the sequence different in the telling of the story?
   What effect does this create?
3 Which is the one most important event? Why?
4 Why do you think the ghost appeared to the writer? Did it have a
   message for her? If so, what was the message?

Character

5 Can you answer these questions about the storyteller?
   – What's her name?
   – How old is she?
   – What does she look like?
   – Is she married?
   – Where's she from?
   – Does she have a job?
   – Has she got any children?
   Is the missing information important? Why doesn't the storyteller
   tell us more about herself?
6 What do you know about the storyteller's feelings? How do you
   think she feels about living alone? What does she like about the
   fells? And the people who live there?
7 Why do we know more about her thoughts and her reactions than
   we do about her life and appearance? What do we learn about
   her during the story? Does she change in any way? Why does she
   decide to go to Hong Kong at the end of the story? What is she
   afraid of?
8 Think about the ghost. What do Rose and the storyteller have in
   common? What similarities are there in their lives?
9 Who are the other main characters in the story? What do we know
   about them? What do we learn from these characters about a) life
   in the Dales b) the storyteller c) the ghost?
10 Think about the role of dialogue in the story, and what we learn
   about the characters from what they say, what they don't say, and
   how they speak.

Narration

11 The story is told in the first person; how does this affect the style and the atmosphere? What elements would be lost if the story were told by a third-person narrator?

12 Think about how the story starts. Why does it start in the middle? What effect does this have?

13 Think of how the details of Rose's death are delayed until the end of the story. Why does the storyteller do this? What effect does it have?

Atmosphere

14 What are the main elements that help create the atmosphere of mystery and 'otherworldliness' (the possibility of the existence of ghosts)? Think of the time of day, the location of the house, and the general setting.

15 Think of the scene when the storyteller first sees the ghost. What details in the description give this scene its feeling of ghostliness?

16 Describe the ghost. How does she make the storyteller feel, and you, the reader? Did she seem like a ghost?

Style

Similes and metaphors

Both similes and metaphors are used to compare a person or thing with another person or thing. Similes are more direct, and use the prepositions *like* or *as*:

> dahlias staked **like artillerymen**

Here, the writer is describing the flowers as if they were soldiers. The flowers and the soldiers stand in straight, orderly lines. The writer does not need to say this, she suggests it with the simile.

Metaphors are more indirect. They describe a person or thing using language that is normally connected with something very different:

> *I felt minute between the long lines snaking away.*

Here, the writer describes the road as lines. Then, she compares the lines to snakes, moving across the landscape. The effect is that the roads seem to be alive. The use of the metaphor increases the atmosphere of distance and isolation.

17 Look again at the description of the fells at night in the extract below. Look at the words in bold and answer the following questions:
- What is being described?
- What is it being compared to?
- What is the effect?
- What is the overall effect of the description?
- What does it tell us about the storyteller's state of mind?

> *I felt minute between the long lines snaking away, the long low* **undecorated** *horizon, the* **clear hard pencil lines cut with a very sharp hard point**. *Gigantic* **lamp-eyes** *of sheep now and then came shining into the headlights. It was midnight. I did not meet a single car between Mealbeck and Naresby and the* **road ripped** *up and down, narrow and* **sweeping** *and black and quiet.*

18 Look at two extracts from the description of the writer's second encounter with the ghost. What is the woman being compared to? How does this add to the ghostly atmosphere surrounding the woman?

> I   *I looked quickly up and into a big bewildered face, mouth a little open, large bright* **mooning** *eyes. The hair was waved deeply* **like an old Vogue photograph** *and the neckline of the dress was rounded, quite high with a string of pearls.*
>
> II *She was gone, and utterly silently,* **as if I had slept** *for a moment in the sunshine and had a momentary dream. She had seemed* **like a shade**, *a* **classical Greek shade,** *though why I should think of ancient Greece in bleak North Westmorland I did not know.*

19 Are there any other interesting comparisons? Read through the story again. Look particularly at the following: the description of Mealbeck; the storyteller's first encounter with the ghost; the bridge where she stopped her car; the herd of sheep that surrounded the storyteller after she saw the ghost for the second time.

Guidance to the above literary terms, answer keys to all the exercises and activities, plus a wealth of other reading-practice material, can be found on the student's section of the Macmillan Readers website at: www.macmillanenglish.com/readers.

Essay questions

Language analysis

Discuss how two or more of the language areas you've studied help contribute to the telling of TWO or more of the stories in the collection.

Analysing the question

What is the question asking?

It is asking you to:

- choose two or more language areas from the index on page 183
- explain how these language areas function in the context of storytelling in this collection
- use examples from two or more of the stories in the collection as examples.

Preparing your answer

1 Look back through the *Language analysis* sections of the stories you've read and choose two or more languages area that you feel confident about.

2 Make notes about the language areas. Include notes on form, function and use.

3 Choose examples from two stories. Choose examples from both classic and contemporary stories, if possible.

4 Look back at the question and your notes and plan your essay. Use the structure of the question to structure your essay. Here is an example:

Introduction	Introduce the areas you are going to describe.
Main body 1	Explain the general function of the areas you have chosen, use examples from your chosen stories.
Main body 2	Analyse how the areas contribute to the style and atmosphere of both stories, referring to specific passages in the stories.
Conclusion	Summarise the literary uses and functions of the language areas you focused on.

Literary analysis

Choose two stories from this collection. Compare and contrast the atmosphere in the stories, how it is created, and the differences and similarities between them.

Analysing the question

What is the question asking?

It is asking you to:
- look at two stories in the collection
- describe the atmosphere in those stories
- describe the structure, setting and surroundings, language, characters and themes of the story and how they affect the atmosphere
- describe the similarities between the stories, and any differences, and think about how this affects each one's atmosphere.

Preparing your answer

1 Choose two stories that are different enough in atmosphere to allow you to contrast them.
2 Make notes about the atmosphere in those stories; what kind of atmosphere it is and how it is created. Think about the language, the structure of the story, the setting, characters and themes.
3 Find key scenes in the stories where the atmosphere is created and conveyed. Make a note of any useful quotations.
4 Make a list of similarities and differences between the stories, such as the setting, the weather, the time of year, the social environment (city, village, isolated house, etc), historical context, and so on.
5 Read the question again and write an essay plan. Here is an example:

Introduction	Briefly introduce the two stories.
Story 1	Describe the first story and its atmosphere – how is the atmosphere created? What are the important elements that affect the atmosphere?
Story 2	Describe the second story and its atmosphere – how is the atmosphere created? What are the important elements that affect the atmosphere?

Similarities	Discuss the similarities between the atmosphere of the two stories.
Differences	Discuss the differences between the atmosphere of the two stories.
Conclusion	Make a general comment about the importance of the atmosphere in a horror story.

For tips on writing academic essays, and essays about literary analysis, visit the student's section of the Macmillan Readers website at www.macmillanenglish.com/readers.

Glossary

The definitions in the glossary refer to the meanings of the words and phrases as they are used in the short stories in this collection. Some words and phrases may also have other meanings which are not given here. The definitions are arranged in the story in which they appear, and in alphabetical order.

The Terror of Blue John Gap

clinch an argument PHRASE to win an argument

commonplace (adj) *formal* not unusual

explain away PHRASAL VERB to tell someone about something in a way that makes them think it is unimportant, so that they do not ask questions

lurk (v) to wait, sometimes hiding, in order to frighten, annoy or attack someone

make your way PHRASE to start moving towards a place

peer (v) to look very carefully, especially because something is difficult to see

perch (v) to sit on something that is narrow or small, and usually high

riddle (n) someone or something that is mysterious or confusing

rise from the ranks PHRASE to start in a junior position in an organisation and gradually reach a higher position

set down PHRASAL VERB to write something on a piece of paper so that it will not be forgotten and can be looked at later

shrink back PHRASAL VERB to move back or away from someone or something, especially because you are frightened or nervous

soaked (adj) extremely wet

superstitious (adj) believing in the power of magic or luck

track down PHRASAL VERB to find someone or something after a long search

utter (adj) complete: often used for emphasising how bad someone or something is

vow (v) to promise that you will do something

Oh, Whistle and I'll Come, My Lad

catch sight of (v) to see something for a very short time

clear cut (adj) simple and straightforward

commotion (n) noise and confused activity

get to the bottom of something PHRASE to find out the true cause or explanation of a bad situation

in the same boat PHRASE in the same difficult or unpleasant situation

misgiving (n) a feeling of fear or doubt about whether something is right or will have a good result

nudge (v) to give someone a little push with your elbow

pensive (adj) seeming to be thinking carefully about something

pore over PHRASAL VERB to examine or read something very carefully and in a lot of detail

pull yourself together PHRASE to control yourself and behave calmly after being upset, angry, shocked, etc

take up PHRASAL VERB to start doing something regularly as a habit, job or interest

the lie of the land PHRASE the shape of the land around you

to and fro (adv) in one direction and then back again

turn out PHRASAL VERB to be discovered to be something

rig up PHRASAL VERB to make something quickly out of whatever you can find

The Monkey's Paw

at the expense of PHRASE if one thing exists or happens at the expense of another, the second thing suffers or is not done properly because of the first

avaricious (adj) greedy; having a strong feeling that you want a lot of money and possessions and to keep them to yourself

dubiously (adv) not sure about the truth or quality of something, or whether you should do something

enthralled (adj) so interested in or excited by something that you give it all your attention

haste (n) great speed in doing something because of limited time

hush (n) a sudden silence

irony (n) 1 a form of humour in which you use words to express the opposite of what the words really mean; 2 a strange, funny, or sad situation in which things happen in the opposite way to what you would expect

jar (v) to be unsuitable in an unpleasant way in a particular place or situation

jump to conclusions PHRASE to make a decision about something too quickly without knowing all the facts

knowing glance NOUN PHRASE if you give someone a knowing glance you look at them in a way that shows that you know about something

mar (v) to spoil something

screw up your courage PHRASE to prepare mentally for doing something difficult

spell (n) words or actions that are intended to make magic things happen

strike a match PHRASE to light a match

torrent (n) 1 a fast and powerful flow of liquid, especially water; 2 a large amount of something, especially something unpleasant, eg abuse, words or criticism

unwholesome (adj) something which is not healthy, or not good for you

weep (v) to cry because you feel unhappy or have some other strong emotion

Smoke Ghost

amount to something PHRASAL VERB to be of some importance

back and forth PHRASE moving first in one direction and then in the other direction, very fast

bewilder (v) to make someone feel confused

bleak (adj) without any reasons to feel happy or hopeful

paint a bleak picture PHRASE to describe something in a way which is not hopeful or optimistic

charlatan (n) someone who cheats people by claiming that they have special knowledge or abilities

cower (v) to move your body down and away from someone or something because you are frightened

crop up PHRASAL VERB *informal* if a name or subject crops up, someone mentions it

distraught (adj) extremely worried, upset or confused

dread (v) to feel very worried about something that is going to happen

flop (v) to sit or lie down in a heavy way by relaxing your muscles relax and letting your body fall

get into hot water PHRASE get into trouble because of something you have done

get your hooks into something PHRASE *informal* to get someone and keep them in a situation that is bad for them

gyrate (v) to move around quickly in circles

hitch (v) to move a part of your body or something you are carrying to a higher position

loom up (v) to appear as a large shape that is not clear, usually in a threatening way

loose ends PHRASE minor unresolved problems

lurch (v) to move suddenly in a way that is not smooth or controlled

morbid (adj) showing a strong interest in subjects such as death that most people think are unpleasant

mutter (v) to talk in a quiet voice that is difficult to hear, especially because you are annoyed or embarrassed or talking to yourself

overwrought (adj) extremely emotional or upset

pamper (v) giving something more importance than it deserves

pin your hopes on something PHRASE to hope very much that someone or something will succeed when everyone or everything else has failed

prestigious (adj) admired and respected by people

pry (v) to be interested in someone's personal life in a way that is annoying or offensive

rasping (adj) unpleasant sound as though two rough things were rubbing together, especially when speaking or breathing

rattle (v) *informal* to make someone feel nervous or angry

shrewd (adj) able to judge people and situations very well and to make good decisions

skimp (v) to spend too little time or attention on a job

take a load off my mind PHRASE to stop worrying about something

tight-lipped (adj) refusing to comment on something

unburden (v) to tell someone about your problems so that you feel less worried about them

wince (v) to react to something with an expression on your face that shows you are embarrassed or feel pain

A Spot of Gothic

back and forth PHRASE moving first in one direction and then in the other direction, very fast

beckon (v) to signal to someone to come towards you

be cut off PHRASE to lose your electric power or phone line

brood (v) to think and worry about something a lot

career (v) to move forwards very quickly in an uncontrolled way

cram (v) to put people or things in a space that is too small

down-to-earth (adj) practical and sensible

fit in PHRASAL VERB to belong to a group or community

flap (v) to move something quickly up and down

fuss (v) to behave in a way that shows you are nervous or worried

give yourself airs PHRASE to behave in a way that is not natural and relaxed in order to impress people and seem important

hang back PHRASAL VERB to not do something immediately because you are not confident or you do not feel certain about it

hurtle (v) to move very quickly, especially in an uncontrolled way

minute (adj) extremely small

neglected (adj) the failure to give someone or something the care and attention they need

no-nonsense (adj) doing things quickly and effectively without worrying too much about other people's feelings

overgrown (adj) covered with plants that have been allowed to grow in an uncontrolled way

reckless (adj) not thinking about the possible bad consequences of your actions

rickety (adj) unstable, likely to break if you put any weight on it

see someone off PHRASAL VERB to go somewhere such as a station or airport with someone in order to say goodbye to them

take something in PHRASAL VERB to understand and absorb a fact or situation

to be the soul of something PHRASE to be the perfect example of a particular quality, eg 'she is the soul of discretion'

totter (vb) to stand or move in a way that is not steady

tremendous (adj) extremely good, important or strong

wag (v) to shake your finger or head from side to side, usually to show you are angry

whizz (v) *informal* to move or travel very quickly

yell (v) to say something in a loud voice

Dictionary extracts adapted from the Macmillan English Dictionary © Macmillan Publishers Limited 2002

Language study index